YOUNG PEOPLE AND DRINKING

Young People and Drinking

THE USE AND ABUSE OF BEVERAGE ALCOHOL

DR. ARTHUR H. CAIN

THE JOHN DAY COMPANY

NEW YORK

The John Day Company, 257 Park Avenue South, New York N.Y. 10010
an Intext publisher

Published on the same day in Canada by Longman Canada Limited.

Library of Congress Catalogue Card Number: 62-20792
Printed in the United States of America
Eleventh Printing

In Memoriam

To E. M. JELLINEK, D.Sc.

Whose pioneering work in the field of Education on Alcohol has been an invaluable well of information—and inspiration—to all who have followed him.

It is our belief that the colleges, together with the high schools and universities, can fulfill a highly significant function in aiding our society to achieve a firmer, more effective, and better integrated morality concerning drinking and its related problems. One of the prerequisites for reaching this goal is to develop well-oriented, disciplined and relevant knowledge and present it to the younger generation in objective and intelligible, organized, and emotionally meaningful fashion.

from *Drinking in College*
Selden D. Bacon and
Robert Straus
(Yale University Press,
New Haven, 1953.)

Contents

Teen-Age Drinking: Whose Responsibility?

The average young person in this country starts experimenting with drinking at about age 17. There are subtle references to the subject, tastes now and then of alcoholic beverages, and trial runs with a little beer, wine, or a sip of a cocktail. The olive from a parent's martini may already have become a ritual.

How shall we go about teaching a teen-ager about drinking—the good points, if there are any, and the dangers which are obvious to most of us? How do we impress upon a youth what drinking means, its risks, its effects and its dangers?

Everyone does not react alike. Some people should *never* drink. About 10 percent of all alcoholics, for instance, have trouble early in their lives, dating from the first drink. In some people, alcohol invariably produces adverse effects or always results in excessive drinking. It is obvious that such people should not drink at all, at any time, for their own sakes and their families.

What of the others, however—those who do not have immediate adverse results? How are young people to learn that in alcohol we are dealing with a very powerful agent, which is used wisely and with control and propriety by some, but by others is used indiscriminately, without control and good judgment?

Alcohol can give a feeling of exhilaration, a sense of power, superiority, and grandiosity. But this power is unreal and elusive; it is the power of the alcohol, not of the drinker. When a person drinks only to get this power, there is danger.

It is imperative that young people learn to live realistically in a real world. When they drink to get a lift, to enjoy the envy of their friends, or to acquire a sense of grandeur, they are drinking to escape into unreality. The euphoria, the feeling of well-being, the sense of increased power, the lack of care and responsibility— all of which is much more pleasant than facing drab reality— can be very attractive. But it is of no value when preparing for future living.

The basic values must be taught. The realization that with every act there is an accompanying responsibility and the necessity for assuming this responsibility must be the basic factor if a person is to drink.

It is urgent that every youth learn about alcohol, know its physiological actions in the body, know how his body reacts to it. If it affects him adversely, he should learn to avoid it, especially when such adversity comes consistently with his drinking.

If he can control his drinking so that at no time he allows the alcohol to control him, then he may use it as many do, in appropriate social situations. If, however, he drinks for the effect it gives him, for the boost it gives his ego, for the courage he needs and without which he cannot face his problems, then indeed alcohol is no longer a beverage, but a drug to give him something artificially which he does not himself possess.

These are the danger signs, and young people must be warned so they can recognize them.

Education in the public schools, particularly in high schools, should give our children the true scientific facts about alcohol.

These can be taught in many courses—general science, biology, physical education, health courses, as well as in the social sciences. The most important thing to be learned is that control is an absolute requirement. The slightest indication of loss of such control calls for complete abstinence.

Where drinking becomes a necessity in order to carry on, that individual should be detected early and taught how to face life's problems without depending on a drug.

The respect for abstinence in others must also be learned by young people. Those who do not drink have a right to their abstinence without appearing inadequate. Refusal to drink by anyone must be considered a free choice, to be respected.

When such facts are generally taught, when the schools and the teachers in the schools understand the importance of the problem of alcoholism, and when the teaching is as seriously regarded for drinking as it is in many areas today regarding driving, then perhaps there will be sufficient knowledge disseminated so that alcoholism in future generations may be prevented.[1]

Marvin A. Block, m. d.
Chairman, Committee on Alcoholism (1954–64)
American Medical Association

[1] From *Today's Health,* published by the American Medical Association.

INTRODUCTION

This book is not a sermon on "the evils of drink." Far from it. We know that people have used beverages containing the chemical called "alcohol" almost from the beginning of recorded history. We know, too, that *almost half* of the people in the United States today drink beverage alcohol in one form or another—even if it's only a little wine to celebrate festival occasions once a year.

As we grow up, we all have to decide what we, as individual, thinking persons are going to do about drinking. We see signs of drinking all around us every day—in ads, in liquor store windows, in bars and cocktail lounges. Perhaps it is served by the adults in our homes.

Yet, we hear very different stories about alcohol. Some people seem to take it for granted—as an ordinary part of our daily life, like dining, dancing, or going to the theater. Other people seem to be violently opposed to drinking alcohol beverages in any form. We are told that we may become "alcoholics" if we drink; that is, we might become "addicted" to alcohol just like those sick people who have fallen into the habit of taking drugs.

What to think? Even more important, what to do?

What we want to do in this book is to give young people the FACTS about drinking, both normal drinking and excessive drinking, so that they can decide for themselves what they want to do about it. We know that there is no part of growing up that is more confusing than the problem of drinking. It is something that has long been a subject for all kinds of superstitious beliefs, emotional opinions, and downright ignorance. And since drinking is definitely a fact of life that we have to face sooner or later, face it with all the facts at hand and with clear heads and onsciences.

Some of the things we shall discuss are:

1. *The chemical nature of alcohol.* Is it a *stimulant,* like coffee or tea, or a *pain-killer,* like aspirin? Is an alcoholic beverage nourishing, like food? Is it poisonous?
2. *What kinds of drinks are there to choose from?* What's the difference between beer and ale? The many kinds of wine, whiskey, gin, brandy, and other "hard liquors." Their relative strengths. *When* to drink *what—if* you drink.
3. *Some arguments in favor of moderate, social drinking.* Possible social advantages, relaxation.
4. *Some arguments against drinking.* Athletics and alcohol. Drinking and driving. Possible social *dis*advantages of drinking. Delinquency and alcohol. Health. Sex and drinking.
5. *What is alcoholism?* Could you become an alcoholic? Do you know any "problem drinkers" (people who drink too much and can't seem to stop)? Is there anything that can be done to help them?

Finally, we shall sum up what we have learned and take stock of the drinking situation as it applies to you, personally. You can give yourself a little I.Q. test concerning drinking. Then—with all the facts and figures at your fingertips—you can make up your mind what you want to do about it: drink or not drink; be a drinker who knows what he (or she) is doing; or a non-drinker—who has learned that it's no longer considered "smart" to drink just to keep from being called a poor sport or a prude.

We know that you, armed with this knowledge, will be master of alcohol, not its slave through ignorance—no matter what decision your good judgment dictates for you.

Here's to happy reading, and to sane drinking—or total abstention—as the case may be!

YOUNG PEOPLE AND DRINKING

CHAPTER 1

What *Is* Alcohol?

> In our society today there are many attitudes toward drinking. We all have the responsibility of interpreting the society in which young people must function. If the use of alcohol constitutes an unresolved issue in our culture then we must explore constructive attitudes with respect to the use and abuse of alcohol, with the hope that the next generation will have a sound attitude on drinking customs.
>
> —RAYMOND G. McCARTHY, Director
> Division of Alcoholism
> Department of Mental Hygiene
> State of New York.

In the old days, from the turn of the century to the beginning of World War I (1900–1915), about the only education people received about alcohol beverages came from the so-called "temperance leagues." These were groups of men and women opposed to the use of such beverages, for various reasons. Drunkenness was, of course, their main objection to drinking.

But they did not present their arguments very scientifically. One famous story concerns the lecture being given a group of homeless derelicts in a mission house of a big eastern city. The lecturer, imposingly equipped with blackboard, pointer and what appeared to be a chemistry set, was preparing to prove that alcohol is a *poison* and therefore should not be consumed by human beings—at least not by intelligent ones.

When he reached the dramatic climax of his demonstration he produced two glasses—and a live garden-variety worm. In one glass there was ordinary drinking water, H_2O. In the other a small quantity of alcohol, C_2H_5OH, had been added.

The worm was dropped into the first glass. No ill effects; the worm swam about happily (and, presumably, soberly). Then the same worm was dropped into the second glass, the one containing alcohol.

After a few moments of threshing about, our poor worm gave up, sank to the bottom—and died.

The lecturer was always triumphant, until one old character in the back row rose unsteadily to his feet and said, "Well, sir, that proves it all right! *When you've got worms, drink whiskey!*"

And frankly, he was making about as much sense as the lecturer. What we are concerned with when we begin the study of alcoholic beverages is, first, alcohol's nature as a chemical which has been produced naturally since the beginning of our world as we know it now, and its effects on human beings, not animals. We know, of course, that it's not a poison in the ordinary sense of the word. Many people drink it every day without dying or even getting sick. On the other hand, it does seem to be "poisonous" for certain people, who become seriously ill whenever they touch the stuff.

Well, let's start at the beginning—and we'll be scientific about it.

How Did It All Begin?

Nature produces alcohol by a process known as fermentation. This means that when certain foodstuffs such as cereals, fruits, or juices are allowed to remain in a warm place for any length of time, a significant change will occur. Living cells (yeast) begin to convert the sugar in the foodstuff into alcohol. This process will continue until there is no more sugar left, or until there is so much alcohol that it stops the yeast from working.

This kind of alcohol is called *ethyl* alcohol. It is sometimes loosely referred to as *grain* alcohol, simply because most whiskies and beers are made from grains such as rye, wheat, barley, and corn. Ethyl alcohol is the only kind which may be safely consumed internally by humans. Other forms of alcohol include *methyl* and *butyl* alcohol, which are poisonous and are used for medical and industrial purposes such as rubbing alcohol and the antifreeze we put in our cars to keep radiators from freezing.

Since ethyl alcohol is derived mostly from grains and fruits, which are foods, it follows naturally that alcohol itself is a food. (We shall confine ourselves henceforth to the study of ethyl alcohol alone. Therefore, when we say "alcohol" we mean ethyl alcohol.) It is not a very good food, however. It is top-heavy in calories, the unit of measurement used in determining the heat-producing or energy-producing value of food to the human body. But it is woefully deficient in vitamins and minerals, containing practically none of these essential nutrients.

ACTION OF ALCOHOL ON THE BODY

Unlike most foods, alcohol does not have to be digested before it passes into the small intestine. A small amount of it will be absorbed directly into the bloodstream through the stomach wall. From the small intestine it is absorbed very rapidly and carried by the bloodstream to every part of the body. It cannot be stored up in the body for any length of time like some foods but circulates throughout the body until it is *oxidized,* or combined with oxygen to be transferred into heat.

The rate of absorption depends upon a number of complicating factors, such as the condition of the stomach when the beverage is consumed. If there is food in the stomach the rate of absorption will be slower than upon an empty stomach. The *kind* of beverage makes a difference, too: ale or beer, for example, are absorbed somewhat more slowly than whiskey or gin because these drinks still contain some of their cereal products. The stronger the drink (the higher percentage of alcohol in the drink) the longer it will take for the body to burn it up.

About a half-ounce of alcohol (the equivalent of about an ounce of whiskey or gin) will be oxidized by the average sized person in about an hour.

Practically no alcohol as such is eliminated by the kidneys, by the bowels, or by the sweat glands. We have to burn it up in the blood.

Finally, we come to an all-important fact which we shall be returning to many times during the rest of our discussion. For the moment, we shall simply state the physical fact:

> The consumption of alcohol by a person and its absorption in the body may be much faster than the body can oxidize it.

This means simply that alcohol taken rapidly will "pile up" temporarily in the body. A large amount of nonoxidized alcohol in the body produces *intoxication*.

STIMULANT OR DEPRESSANT?

First, let us examine the question whether alcohol is a poison. Then we shall proceed to more specific classifications of the chemical.

The word "poison" cannot be used meaningfully without specifying the *concentration* of the ingredient. Ordinary table salt or even water, if taken in great excess by an organism, can be fatal, therefore "poisonous." The dictionary definition, which is usually what we mean when we use the word, is simply: "Any agent which, introduced into an organism, may produce an injurious or deadly effect."

Is alcohol a poison, then?

Obviously, the answer is both Yes and No. Taken in relatively small amounts . . . No. Taken in large amounts (especially when taken rapidly, thus increasing the percentage of concentration) . . . Yes. In fact, the medical definition of the word "intoxication" means "a poisoning, as by a spirituous substance." The word "toxic" is from the Latin *toxicum,* meaning poison.

For practical purposes, all we need know in this connection about beverage alcohol at this point is that it *can* be poisonous, and should be treated with respect. There are many cases on record of persons drinking large amounts of spirituous liquor at one time, perhaps a pint at one drink (usually on a bet), and dying almost immediately of acute alcohol poisoning. Small children have been known to drink deadly amounts of beverage alcohol.

More specifically, it is extremely important that we get a clear understanding of how alcohol is classified pharmaceutically; that is, how it is listed among the various drugs which human beings take from time to time. And alcohol is just as much a drug as is the aspirin the doctor might give us for a headache, or even the small amount of caffeine contained in our morning cups of coffee or tea.

But once again we must be careful in defining our terms. Again we must specify what amounts—what concentrations—of alcohol we are talking about.

Scientifically speaking, we can make the following classifications of ethyl alcohol, based upon the quantities indicated:

IN SMALL AMOUNTS, alcohol is an analgesic or pain-killer —the direct opposite of stimulant. It is thus an anesthetic, a substance capable of causing partial or complete loss of feeling or sensation. Also in small amounts, it may be called a sedative or "nerve calmer."

IN LARGE AMOUNTS, alcohol can be a narcotic or sleep-producing drug.

We see, therefore, that beverage alcohol, depending upon its usage, could be called an analgesic, a sedative *and* a narcotic. But its main effect, say the experts in pharmacology, is that of a depressant, or anesthetic. Usually it causes partial loss of feeling and sensation.

So . . . we should now be able to define and classify alcohol whenever the occasion arises, bearing in mind that we must first know *how much* alcohol we are talking about.

Yet, if one has already tasted an alcoholic beverage or has observed others after they have taken a drink or two, it certainly *seems* as if the effect of the drink is that of a *stimulant,* doesn't it?

Here's why.

When one takes a drink of fairly strong beverage alcohol, such as a cocktail or a "pony" of straight brandy, there *is* a mild, temporary stimulation of the sensitive tissues of the mouth and tongue; a burning sensation not unlike that experienced when tasting highly seasoned food. A warming sensation may also follow upon the swallowing of such a drink, further giving the impression that we have taken a stimulant. And, very briefly, we might call it that. But in a moment or two this mild, temporary stimulation wears off, and alcohol's depressant action takes over.

Even more dramatic is the way some people *behave* after a few drinks. They become excited, animated, and sometimes, quite gay and boisterous. Is this not the effect of a stimulant? Aren't these people stimulated? They surely don't seem depressed!

But, physically speaking, they *are* depressed—believe it or not. What is happening here is that the drinking person is reacting psychologically to his partial loss of control over his behavior—which is caused by the depressant action of the alcohol he has consumed. And, as you probably know, this excited, animated,

gay behavior doesn't last very long; then the opposite sort of behavior sets in: the drinker becomes dull, sad, or sometimes even
indulges in what has been called a "crying jag."

In other words, enough alcohol absorbed into the body over a
period of time short enough to produce the "piling up" we mentioned previously, causes our normal "controls" to "go on strike"
and we begin to feel a deceptive sense of freedom and excite-
ment. This, as we shall see, can be either good or bad. For the
moment we merely want to learn what happens to us physically
when we have a sufficient concentration of alcohol in our blood-
streams to produce the effect of stimulation. It is, in short, the
apparent contradiction (nonetheless true) of a depressant drug
temporarily causing the illusion of stimulation.

ALCOHOL AS MEDICINE

Until fairly recently, many families always made it a custom to
keep a little spirituous liquor on hand in case of illness. It was
administered for almost everything from bad colds to chills and
attacks of nerves. In fact, most men wouldn't think of going on a
fishing or hunting trip without a bottle of strong drink along in
case of *snakebite!*

Today, alcohol is generally considered to have little value as
medicine. It cannot cure a cold, and in fact, may even make it
worse. As we have already seen, the warming effect of alcohol is
a temporary feeling at best and can even be dangerous, as we
may become seriously chilled without realizing it. As for a snakebite remedy, it is the *worst* thing we could do.

So, we'll have to disregard most well-intended but outdated advice some people may have to give us about the medicinal effects
of alcohol.

On the other hand, many people will be surprised to find that
alcohol, in moderation of course, has very few, if any, adverse
effects on the human body.

There are many old wives' tales about the dreadful damage alcohol beverages do to the drinker. The most popular superstition, still held by many, is that even moderate drinking will *inevitably* cause cirrhosis of the liver, a condition characterized by the hardening of that organ due to the formation of excessive connecting tissues. (We'll make clear exactly what we mean by "moderate drinking" after a while.) It is not bad on the heart, the stomach, the lungs, or any other part of the body—always with the provision "used in moderation," and pointing out that we are still talking about the direct action of alcohol on the body. *In*directly, a great many things can happen to us due to drinking, but that is another story.

But, you may ask, what about that well-known fact of *overindulgence* commonly known as the "hangover"? Maybe you have never experienced this never-to-be-forgotten condition yourself, but you have, perhaps, seen others who are suffering from too much to drink. If these people are as sick as they claim to be, surely then alcoholic beverages must be bad for one physically.

For the ordinary, common hangover—the kind suffered by the average American drinker perhaps once a year (more often than not following some special celebration, such as the big New Year's Eve party)—it can be said that the patient is indeed sick for the duration of his "attack," usually a matter of a few hours. Then, however, he seems to recover completely. There are seldom any continuing ill effects from such a hangover.

During the period of even such a relatively mild hangover, however, the sufferer's symptoms are really quite severe, and it seems almost a shame that he gets so little sympathy for his plight. He has a severe headache, which aspirin and other remedies will mask slightly without offering real relief. He is nauseated and cannot eat. He is dizzy; his mouth is dry; and he is extremely thirsty but water seems to make him feel even worse. He is so weak that he can hardly summon up enough strength to walk, let alone work or study.

And, unfortunately, there is the sad old saying: There is no cure for a hangover but death! Seriously, Time, the Great Healer, is about the only thing that does much good.

These severe aftereffects of overindulgence result from the "piling up" condition we have already explained. Too much alcohol is absorbed into the body at such a fast rate that it cannot be oxidized. There is not much he can do except wait for the slow process of oxidation to burn up the remaining alcohol. In the meantime, digestion is impaired, and the entire function of the body is slowed down to a painful degree.

And, as we mentioned before, if you should be a victim of the common hangover, don't expect to get much sympathy from your fellow students or friends or neighbors. They know that it's not going to last long, and that you probably won't suffer any lasting damage from your experience. They also know that all your woes and miseries were self-inflicted, and they'll be inclined to laugh rather than commiserate with you for your sad condition.

About the only good thing one can say for the hangover is that it serves as an excellent warning signal: it tells the drinker not to drink so much next time, and it tells him not to drink at all for a long time to come. For many, one really bad hangover is enough to make him ask himself the question: Was it worth it? And perhaps he will think twice before inflicting this agony upon himself at all, ever again.

But in all honesty, it must be said that serious or lasting physical harm is seldom incurred from an ordinary hangover. Once again, though, we must point out that we are still talking about direct physical damage to the body, not possible side effects. As a matter of fact, it stands to reason that if one drinks enough to cause the severe physical symptoms we call the hangover, one is also probably exposing himself to a number of much more serious consequences before the drinking ends and the hangover sets in. Probably the most serious and dramatic danger signal in this respect stems from the fact that one's *memory* is temporarily impaired to some extent after such overindulgence and we can't be quite sure exactly what kind of trouble we did get into the night before!

However, when a person drinks but does not overindulge (we shall consider precise measurements and situations later which will serve as guides to how one can safely stop short of overdoing it), there seems to be little indication that the alcohol ingested has much effect one way or another, good or bad. Some think that a little alcohol before a meal helps the appetite and digestion, but this is hardly a major consideration for the young American today; he's usually ravenous enough at mealtime without a drink to make him even hungrier. It's quite possible, too, for a pre-meal drink to dull one's appetite rather than whet it.

By and large, then, it is probably just as well for the young person considering drinking to forget about any great physical dangers of moderate drinking—and benefits as well. Neither are important enough to influence one's general attitude toward drinking either way.

One word of caution: there are, of course, those persons who, for one reason or another, should not drink beverage alcohol at all for physical reasons.

IN ALL CASES the individual person should seek the advice of a physician before he does any drinking at all. In most cases the doctor will advise the young person to postpone his drinking until he is quite mature physically, and then to start very cautiously and experimentally to determine if he has any unusual reactions to the ingestion of alcohol.

Makes sense, doesn't it? And the doctor will admire your good sense in asking him about it.

Now, let us review what we have learned about alcohol and its effects on the human body. On the next page we have prepared a little quiz, an "Alcohol-Quotient" test, for you to determine how knowledgeable and sophisticated you have become on the

subject. Answer the questions to the best of your ability, then
check back through the present chapter to see if you were right
or wrong.

ALCOHOL QUOTIENT TEST

1. The production of the chemical called "alcohol" is:
   (   ) a. An artificial process
   (•) b. A natural process
   (   ) c. Forbidden by law in some states
2. The alcohol contained in alcohol beverages is:
   (•) a. Ethyl alcohol
   (   ) b. Methyl alcohol
   (   ) c. Butane alcohol
3. From the standpoint of human nutrition, beverage alcohol is:
   (   ) a. An excellent food
   (   ) b. Well balanced but fattening
   (•) c. High in calories; low in vitamins and minerals
4. Alcohol is:
   (   ) a. Hard to digest
   (•) b. Needs no digesting
   (   ) c. Digested slowly by the stomach
5. Alcohol can be handled by:
   (•) a. Everyone equally, regardless of size
   (   ) b. Larger persons better than smaller ones
   (   ) c. Smaller persons better than larger ones
6. The condition known as "intoxication" means that:
   (   ) a. Alcohol has been absorbed by the body faster than
            it can burn it up
   (•) b. The body has been poisoned
   (   ) c. Alcohol in any amount causes intoxication
7. Alcohol is eliminated from the body chiefly by:
   (   ) a. The lungs, kidneys, and sweat glands

(•) b. Oxidation, or burning up by oxygen

( ) c. Regurgitation, or vomiting

8. Medically speaking, alcohol is primarily:

    (•) a. A depressant

    ( ) b. A stimulant

    ( ) c. Neither of these

9. Specifically, pharmacologists classify alcohol as:

    (✓) a. An analgesic, or pain-killer

    ( ) b. A sedative, or nerve-calmer

    ( ) c. An anesthetic causing partial loss of feeling and sensation

10. Ethyl alcohol is:

    ( ) a. A poison, used for commercial purposes

    ( ) b. A tonic, if taken before meals

    (•) c. A poison if taken too quickly in large quantities

11. People under the influence of alcohol seem to be stimulated because:

    ( ) a. Highballs make them "high"

    ( ) b. They are allergic to alcohol

    (•) c. Their "behavior controls" are affected

12. Speaking medicinally, alcohol is:

    ( ) a. A good, general remedy for many illnesses

    ( ) b. Good for snakebite, because if you drink enough you will see snakes and they will be on *your* side because you dreamed them up

    (•) c. Practically useless as an internal medicine

13. As far as physical injury is concerned, alcohol is:

    ( ) a. Harmful to the alimentary canal

    (•) b. In moderation, virtually harmless to most people

    ( ) c. A dangerous drug

14. The best person to consult about drinking is:

    (•) a. Your family doctor

    ( ) b. The nearest bartender

    ( ) c. Your neighborhood pharmacist

If you are really serious about learning something about drinking before you do anything about it, you had better have a score of 100 percent correct—even if some of our optional answers *were* pretty tricky.

Just remember one thing: As far as your central nervous system is concerned, ethyl alcohol is ethyl alcohol, no matter what kind of drink it's in. A milk punch may be more nourishing than a two-ounce drink of straight whiskey, but if it has two ounces of whiskey in it it is just as potent. A Pink Lady or a Sloe Gin fizz may look like, and even taste like, the punch you might be served at a church lawn party. But they'll get you just as intoxicated (and probably sicker) than the infamous Boilermaker, which consists of a double whiskey followed by a beer chaser.

Don't let anybody kid you.

Even more important—*don't try to kid yourself.*

Your bloodstream and your nervous system simply won't buy such a bill of goods.

All set? Now that we have a firm grip on what alcohol is, and what it does to us, let us learn something about the various ways in which it is used, and the many kinds of alcoholic beverages being served today and in the past.

CHAPTER 2

Kinds of Drinks

> The use of alcohol beverages is a very ancient custom. We know from the present distribution of brewed beverages that the brewing of beer was probably discovered almost at the time agriculture itself was discovered. We may presume that the use of natural fermentation to produce wine is even more primitive and ancient.[1]
>
> —DONALD HORTON, Ph.D.

HISTORY OF ALCOHOL PRODUCTION

Alcohol was and still is used throughout the world from East to West. In the *Rig-Veda*, which is honored by Hindus as a divine revelation, the intoxicating drink of the Indian *(soma)* is mentioned, of which nothing is known about its method of preparation. *Sura*, on the other hand, seems to be a kind of brandy. Indians also make a wine from rice which must have been similar to *arrack*, which is drunk in the Middle East today. Distilleries existed at the time of Strabo, the Greek geographer (63 B.C.?–A.D. 24), which satisfied their taste for *soma* and probably for other alcoholic beverages such as *kikala* and *parisroot*.

[1]Donald Horton, *Alcohol, Science and Society,* Quarterly Journal of Studies on Alcohol (1945), New Haven, p. 153.

We have already learned that nature produces alcohol by the fermentation of sugar. It can also be produced by the formation of the starch contained in vegetable matter into dextrose or maltose, and by the distillation of alcoholic liquors.

The first process is the foundation of which the preparation of mead or honey-beer is based. The latter is still extensively in use in Abyssinia (Bitoo, Tej of Amhara, Tadi of Croma), the Galla countries, and in Southwest Africa.

In the first century, Pliny the Elder mentions mead as a drink consisting of water and honey. The best wine, he says, is prepared with rainwater which has previously been set aside for five years. Some people in Pliny's day mixed one-third of rainwater prepared in this way with one-third of fresh or sometimes boiled water, and one-third of old honey.

The *Edda,* a collection of mythological and heroic songs in the Old Norse or Icelandic language dating from between the tenth and thirteenth centuries, states that the dwarfs Fjalar and Galar, after having assassinated the wise Koasin, mixed his blood with honey and prepared a beverage which endowed everyone who drank of it with the gift of song.

The Scandinavians drank mead avidly. They introduced it into England, and because the cup of mead played an important role in the marriage ceremonies which lasted for thirty days, the first month after marriage was called "the honeymoon."

Other strange-sounding and ancient drinks include palm wine, banana wine, and products made from the *agave* plant called *pulque* or *metl.* The juice of certain cactus plants (*ceras giganteus, optuntia tuna,* and *optuntia fecus indicus*) are drunk by Indians and Mexicans in Sonora and Lower California. The people who inhabit the Caspian Sea and Mongolia and eastern Siberia —the Kirghiz, Tekinzes, Buriats and Tungus—have long known how to prepare beverages whose origin is obscure. They use for this purpose mares' milk, of which the lactose is transformed into fermentable sugar. In this way they obtain *kumise,* with 1.5 to 3 percent alcohol. The latter is consumed in great quantities in the oasis of Marv and is called *chal;* in Armenia it is *manun;* and in the language of the Tartars, *katish.*

The second of the general methods adopted in order to obtain alcohol beverages seems to have been first used with millet. An alcoholic millet beer is prepared, for instance, among the Azande of the Congo, in the Mahratta States, and, to a lesser degree, in Nepal.[2] A beer prepared from sorghum is extensively employed in Africa; it is the millet of the Moors and the Kaffirs. Among the Dyaks of Borneo, and to a very large extent in Japan, rice is used for obtaining alcohol by fermentation. And during the Christianization of Peru, exhortations as to the abuse of *chi-chi* formed a large part of the sermons of the missionaries.

The third method, the distillation of alcoholic liquors, is a more advanced scientific development. In those cases where this method was employed by Asiatic peoples of a lesser degree of civilization, they probably gained the knowledge from Europeans, or even, in some cases, from the Chinese. We find in different parts of the world an innumerable variety of distilled spirits. Where potatoes, corn or grapes are not available, man takes other substances containing starch and sugar and prepares distilled spirits by extremely primitive means. The inhabitants of Kamchatka manufacture a very powerful product from hogwood by letting the stems ferment. The natives of Honolulu use the roots of *cordyline terminalis* to the same end. The Indians of eastern Ecuador obtain an alcoholic liquor from the distillation of wasted yucca roots.

Of course, the origin of the technique used to produce wine by natural fermentation is lost in prehistory, but the chances are that it could have been an independent invention, and that it could have appeared simultaneously in different parts of the world because the process itself is so simple. All that would have been

[2] E. E. Evans-Pritchard, *Witchcraft, Oracles, and Magic Among the Azande,* London, Oxford University Press, 1937.

necessary for such a primitive group to discover this potentiality of fruits and vegetables would be open containers or, even before the discovery of the use of pottery, the vessels made of bark which were known to have been used at that time, to obtain a fruit mash and, subsequently, wine of a sort. We know that distillation is relatively recent, probably not coming before the Christian era by very many years, and that it is generally thought that the art of distilling was developed somewhere in India and from there spread throughout the Oriental world and then to the West.

Drinks Popular Today Around The World

Some countries today have their own traditional national beverage.

France, Italy, Spain and other Mediterranean countries consider themselves to be wine-drinking nations. The English drink beer and ale; the Scots, of course, Scotch whisky. (Incidentally, an interesting but little known fact is that domestic whiskey made in the United States is correctly spelled with an "e"; imported whisky, such as Scotch or Irish whisky, without the "e.") The Germanic countries prefer beer. The great drink of the Soviet Union republics is vodka, which is usually made from rye, not potatoes, as is commonly believed. The Japanese, especially prior to World War II, drank *saké*, a wine made from rice. The Chinese have never been great consumers of beverage alcohol in any form, but their version of rice wine, *fa-t'iu*, has been and is still fairly popular.

There is no special national drink in India today, although the now outlawed palm toddy is still consumed in some quantity.[3]

The Arabic countries (Iran, Iraq, Saudi Arabia, Egypt and

[3] Personal observation of the author, 1961.

Syria), and in fact all Moslem countries, have no national alcohol beverage—due to the fact that such beverages are forbidden by the Koran, the holy book of scripture of all believers in Islam. It has been remarked that the Arabic countries form the largest "temperance league" in the world today. Interestingly enough, there is no legal prohibition in most Moslem nations; bars and wine shops are in evidence everywhere.

On the other hand, the new national government of India, whose many different versions of Hinduism, their national religion, do not uniformly forbid the use of alcoholic beverages, has passed prohibition laws in many of its provinces. In Calcutta, for example, alcohol may not be sold publicly on Tuesdays and Fridays. In Bombay—not at all, except to foreigners (and to alcoholics!). In New Delhi, the capital, beverage alcohol may not be consumed publicly, even in one's hotel room.

Most tropical countries, including Central and South America, drink beer. In Mexico, the powerful *tequila*, a liquor distilled from the stems of the century plant, is greatly favored. Many foreigners living in or traveling in tropical countries prefer "gin-and-tonic"—a highball made of gin, which is a strong drink made from grain (usually rye) and juniper berries, and quinine water. The word "tonic" in this instance is a misnomer as tonic water is not really a medicine, as the word seems to imply.

Other favorites around the world today include *ouzo* in Greece, and *arrack* in the Middle East.

Absinthe is now outlawed in nearly all countries due to the fact that it contains oil of wormwood, which may produce mental disturbances. (Pernod is the beverage which has largely replaced absinthe: it is much the same drink with the wormwood removed. The alcohol content, it should be noted, remains approximately the same.)

Drinks Popular Today (The United States)

In terms of quantities of beverage alcohol consumed by persons of drinking age in the United States, beer comes first with some 21.95 gallons consumed per year per person; distilled spirits are next with about 1.90 gallons per person; and wine comes last with about 1.3 gallons. This amounts to an average of about 2.07 gallons of alcohol consumed by each person of drinking age each year.

The above figures are significant because of the fact that we, as a people, seem to prefer spirits to wine. The reverse is true of most other countries in the world.

Now before going into a brief discussion of particular drinks most often served in the U. S. today, rather than just types of alcohol beverages (wines, beers, spirits) it is important that we learn something about the relative strengths of the three main categories of drinks. What do these drinks "do" to the people who drink them?—That is the all-important question.

Beer is the mildest of our three main categories. Most American beers contain from 3 to 6 percent alcohol. This includes ale, stout, and porter, which are simply beers of different colors and tastes. The average American beer is about 4.5 percent alcohol, ✳ by volume.

Wine in America contains 12 to 14 percent alcohol, because the process of fermentation usually ceases naturally at that point. Wines in which the sugar content has largely disappeared are called "dry" wines (*sec* is the French word frequently used); sweet wines (Fr. *brut*) contain a certain amount of sugar. Some wines, however, have been "fortified" with an alcohol solution, sometimes by the admixture of liquors, and run as high as 18 to ✳ 20 percent alcohol.

In America, manufacturers and distributors of both wines and distilled beverages are required by law to show the percentage of alcohol contained in each bottle, and the drinker must be guided by this in every case. If fairly large quantities of wine are consumed within a brief period of time, the difference between 13 percent in the case of unfortified wine and the 19 percent of the stronger product can be, it is easy to see, an extremely important consideration for the drinker—especially to the inexperienced imbiber who is not sure of his own capacity for beverage alcohol.

Distilled spirits (whiskey, gin, rum, brandy, vodka and others) ⚹ consist chiefly of alcohol and water—flavored artificially or by the product from which they are made. *Most contain from 40 to 50* ⚹ *percent alcohol—by far the strongest drinks of our three main categories of beverages.* Percentages of these drinks are usually expressed in terms of "Proof," meaning the minimum percentage of alcohol contained in the beverage at 60 degrees Farenheit; or in the United States, one-half of the percentage by volume. Thus a beverage containing *40 percent* alcohol will be classified as "80 proof"; 45 percent equals 90 proof, and so on. "Bonded" liquor is liquor "bottled in bond" under U. S. Government supervision to guarantee that it is a full 100 proof. Such liquors are sealed with green labels; non-bonded liquors with red labels.

So much for the relative strengths of beverages, expressed in terms of the percentages of alcohol they contain. And—this is most important to remember—*nothing else matters* as far as intoxicating elements in the beverage are concerned. One 90-proof drink is just as intoxicating as any other 90-proof drink, no matter what it is or what superstitions might surround it. How they are mixed and when they are consumed make a great deal of difference, of course; but these are different matters and will be discussed in due course. The first thing to learn, and to remember, is that it is the *alcohol* in the beverage that intoxicates, nothing else. The degree of intoxication incurred depends first of all on the amount of alcohol consumed.

All clear thus far?

We shall proceed another step further then. How, specifically, are these beverages bottled and served in the U. S. today? What can we expect when we are first introduced to ethyl alcohol? Or if we have already become acquainted, what is the precise nature of the drink or drinks with which we have become familiar?

Taking beer first, there is 1) bottled or canned beer; and 2) draught (pronounced "draft") beer, meaning that it is drawn from kegs or barrels. They are the same as far as percentages of alcohol contained are concerned. Beer bottles usually contain 12 ounces of beer; most bars serve glasses of draft beer varying between 8 and 10 ounces. Thus when one drinks the average-sized glass of beer (or ale, porter, or stout) he is consuming about 9 ounces of beer containing about 4.5 percent alcohol.

"Light" beers or "dark" beers refer to their colors, of course. "Light" in this case does not mean "mild." (During Prohibition in the United States there was great agitation for a time to have "light wines and beers" made legal, and for awhile a beer which came to be called "Three-Two" (because it was only 3.2 percent alcohol in content) was sold in some states after Prohibition was repealed. Also, an illegal beverage known as "home-brew"—so-called for obvious reasons—was widely sold. Its alcohol content might be almost any percent; no one ever knew—until, waking up with a splitting headache, it was too late to do anything about it.

There are, of course, a great many special kinds and brands of beer: bock beer, Pilsener beer, and so on. All these are variations of the basic drink we have described under the heading of beer, however, and it is a matter of personal preference as to which one should drink at any given time. Many of these products are named after the localities in which they were originally brewed. Pilsener, for example, is named for a city located southwest of Prague, Czechoslovakia (formerly Bohemia).

It needs only to be added that a persistent but completely false belief to the effect that it is "almost impossible" to become really intoxicated on beer should be disregarded. A ten-ounce glass of beer is the rough equivalent of an ounce of whiskey or gin, no matter what is said about it. If five "shots" of whiskey or five martinis taken over a period of two hours will make a person become intoxicated, then five ten-ounce glasses of beer over the same period of time will inevitably do likewise.

Don't be fooled by superstitions concerning alcohol. There is no area of man's behavior in the history of the world more surrounded by myth and superstition than the use of beverage alcohol. We shall explode some of the more prevalent misconceptions as we go along.

Now let us consider a few of the many kinds of wine that are commonly served in the United States today.

First of all, it is well to be aware that there are two basic wines in the U. S. today: port and sherry.

Port is a fortified wine of rich taste and aroma, usually dark red, which came originally from Oporto (now Porto), Portugal.

Sherry, also a fortified wine, came from Spain, and gets its name from the city of Jerez de la Frontera, where it is made. It is a "still" wine, meaning that it is not "sparkling." Sparkling wines are obtained by bottling them before fermentation is complete, and also by adding carbon dioxide after the end of fermentation.

Dry sherry is an *appetizer wine,* and is served chilled before meals, with light snacks, and at parties. "Cocktail" sherry falls in this category too.

"Ruby" port or "tawny" port is served at the end of the meal with desserts, fruits, cakes and sweet snacks. These are classified as *dessert wines* as compared with the above-mentioned appetizer wines.

Also falling into the appetizer category are both *dry vermouth* and *sweet vermouth:* white wines flavored with aromatic herbs. Incidentally, vermouth is pronounced vair-*mooth'* in this country, and *vur'*-mooth by the British.

The so-called *table* wines are usually divided into three separate categories, according to *color:*

a) *Red* Table Wines: *Burgundy* and *Claret.* Served with meals, at room temperature. Burgundy and claret are served with the heavier foods, such as meats, chops, hams, spiced dishes, and cheese.

b) *Pink* Table Wines: the *rosé* wines—*vin rosé* (pronounced *van rosay,* after the French). These are served chilled with meals. They may be served with almost any kind of food.

c) *White* Table Wines: Sauterne (so-*turn*), Rhine wine, Chablis (sha-*blee*). Served with meals, chilled, or in tall cool drinks.

Sparkling wines—champagne and sparkling burgundies—are correctly served either before, during, or after meals and on almost any occasion.

The dessert wines, the various kinds of port, cream sherries, and muscatel are, as the word "dessert" indicates, served at the end of meals and with sweet foods.

The above listings are, of course, necessarily brief and sketchy. There are many, many varieties of wines in all these categories. But these are the basic wines and their correct uses.

We come now to the use of spirituous liquors, and things immediately become more complex.

The origin and manufacture of spirituous liquors, or distilled spirits, have been discussed already in our chapter on the production of alcohol beverages. Some of the main categories of these drinks are: whiskey, gin, brandy and rum. Let us take them one at a time and examine them carefully. As we know already, this category contains the most powerful of the alcohol beverages in terms of concentration of alcohol itself. For this reason we will be well advised to devote especially careful attention to these drinks. In many respects a martini, for instance, should be treated with the same cautious respect a sensible person accords a loaded revolver.

Whiskey. There are several different kinds of whiskey. We have already mentioned the most famous of them, *Scotch whisky,* a principal export of Scotland. Others include Irish whisky, and the two main American whiskies: rye and bourbon. Bourbon, so called because it is made in Bourbon County, Kentucky, is made of corn. Most whiskies contain from 40 to 50 percent alcohol.

There is also a quite notorious product of the Southlands known simply as "corn" or, more colorfully, "corn likker"—not to mention "white lightning" and "blind tiger." This is a powerful product made by distilling the fermented mash of corn. Although there are corn whiskies legally bottled and sold in the United States, corn liquor gained most of its fame during Prohibition when it was widely produced by the stills of hillbillies in the mountainous Southern regions, particularly the Blue Ridge Mountains of Kentucky, the Virginias, the Carolinas, Georgia, Tennessee and Alabama.

There is an amusing anecdote to the effect that the writer, historian and geographer Carl Carmer thought of the title of his famous book, *Stars Fell on Alabama,* when he first sampled corn whiskey while traveling in that state.

Another little story may serve to illustrate the potency of some alcohol beverages, and at the same time show the extremes some people will go to when it comes to this most anecdotal of man's social activities.

One day in Mississippi—the one remaining state which retains partial prohibition, although there are several which have "dry" counties (there is a saying even in Mississippi, however, to the effect that "the State is dry; but the people aren't!")—a motorist picked up a hitchhiker.

After driving a few miles the hitchhiker produced a pistol and made the driver stop his car. He then brought out a dubious-looking bottle filled with bootleg whiskey.

"Here!" said the hitchhiker, "take a drink!"

The motorist protested that he didn't want a drink, but the hitchhiker flourished his pistol and he reluctantly choked down a few swallows of the liquor.

When he regained his breath and wiped the tears from his eyes, the hitchhiker smiled at him broadly and said, "Wonderful! Now you hold the pistol and make *me* take a drink!"

The great American humorist Irvin S. Cobb is alleged to have given the following definition of "corn likker" to the Distiller's Code Authority:

> It smells like gangrene starting in a mildewed silo, it tastes like the wrath to come, and when you absorb a deep swig of it you have all the sensations of having swallowed a lighted kerosene lamp. A sudden violent jolt of it has been known to stop the victim's watch, snap his suspenders and crack his glass eye right across.

As scientists we cannot vouch for the accuracy of Mr. Cobb's description, but we may feel justified in repeating our warning to treat our category of distilled spirits with caution and respect.

All whiskies are made by distilling fermented mashes of grain. Rye, corn, wheat, oats, and barley are the chief products used.

Gin, as we have already mentioned, is a clear liquor of from 40 to 50 percent alcohol content, and is made by distilling a grain mash (especially rye) in pot stills with juniper berries. It is also made from plain or neutral spirits flavored with aromatics.

Brandy is made by distilling wine, and may contain from 40 to 60 percent by volume. The wines from which brandy is made may be produced by fermenting almost any kind of fruit or grape; thus there is an endless variety of brandies. The best known are the two French brandies, made from grape wine: *cognac* (*kohn'*-yak) and *armagnac* (ar-*ma'*-nyak). In the United States we have peach brandy, plum brandy, applejack, cherry brandy—the list is almost inexhaustible.

Rum, because of our proximity to the big sugar-producing countries, is widely used in the United States. It is produced by distilling fermented molasses. Certain rums are among the most potent liquors of all, sometimes running as high as an incredible *90 percent* alcohol, although most rums average be- ✳ tween 40 and 50 percent.*

(An interesting if confusing fact about rum is that the word is sometimes used in American slang to denote any kind of strong drink—whiskey, gin, or whatnot.)

Rum is usually colorless, although sometimes colored by caramel or by the casks in which it is produced. The Caribbean islands of Jamaica and Barbados are believed to produce the best rums. Incidentally, these islands also produce a cosmetic and medicinal fluid known as *bay rum* which is not intended for internal use—although certain types of Skid Row alcoholics (see Chapter Five) have been known to drink it—sometimes with fatal results.

These liquors, or forms of distilled spirits, are, then, the major types of "strong" drinks we are apt to encounter under most circumstances.

They are served in a number of ways, some of them surprisingly complicated—and perhaps hazardous to the uninformed.

First, here are some of the *simple* ways of serving or drinking liquors:

Highballs. A highball is usually whiskey diluted with water, club soda, or ginger ale and served in a tall glass, with ice. It is possible, of course, to make a highball of almost any ingredient—rum, brandy, or any other alcoholic beverage. The mixture is customarily about at a ratio of five to one: five parts mixer to one part whiskey or other liquor. This ratio, it will be noted, makes the highball approximately the same strength as a similar quantity of beer; i.e., a highball consisting of one ounce of whiskey and five ounces of soda has roughly the same alcoholic strength as a ten-ounce glass of beer. By the same arithmetic, a three-ounce

* For obvious reasons, it may pay the beginning drinker to inspect the bottle carefully for alcohol content before drinking rum.

goblet of fortified wine would fall into approximately the same range.

In the same category as highballs are: gin-and-tonic; the Tom Collins (one part gin to about five of soda, with lemon or lime and sugar); and the even simpler drinks of "X-and-water"—Scotch and plain water, for example.

There are many unusual ways of serving spirituous drinks: *frozen daiquiris,* for instance, which are made of rum; *punches* (concocted with various fruits and mixers); and a great many others.

The second most prevalent manner of preparing spirituous drinks, after the fairly simple highball, is the cocktail.

The cocktail has been regarded by many, even in the present day and by staunch advocates of social drinking, not temperance leaguers, as an invention of the devil himself. Yet it continues to be one of the most popular ways to drink, especially in big cities both here and abroad. Just what is the Story of the Cocktail?

A cocktail, first of all, is a short, mixed drink. The main difference between a cocktail and a highball is that the cocktail is mixed with *still another alcoholic beverage*—NOT with water, or soda, or ginger ale. A cocktail is, therefore, *much stronger in alcohol concentration* than a highball of any description.

Furthermore, the cocktail is deliberately designed to *seem* mild, tasty, zestful, piquant—to the taste.

But—and it's a big BUT—*it's the alcohol content that counts* as we've already had occasion to remark, and as we shall be pointing out again and again before our basic education on alcohol is complete.

Let us examine the three most popular cocktails in America today and see what makes them tick—to use a phrase which may be more than appropriate.

First, the famous (or infamous) *martini.* Here is one recipe for a "dry" martini:

One part French Vermouth (Italian Vermouth would make it a *sweet* martini)
Three parts gin
Ice

What's so devilish about this little drink?

Well, in the first place, that cocktail glass is holding perhaps two ounces of liquid altogether. The three parts of gin are a solid 90 proof, or 45 percent alcohol. The single part of vermouth is about 18 percent alcohol. There is nothing except the ice to dilute the drink, and not enough of that melts during the mixing process to make any real difference.

So . . . it's easy to see that what you are drinking is a small bombshell of about 40 percent alcohol—and it looks and tastes like the most innocent of drinks.

One such martini is, however, the equivalent of two large glasses of beer, a large glass of wine, or a large highball. And, as many a remorseful sufferer of the previously described hangover will tell you, it's very easy to drink three or four martinis within an hour—thus enabling the "piling up" process to take place with a vengeance.

Famous last words: "What happened?"

Forewarned is forearmed. And remember the immortal statement a well-known actress made when her teen-age daughter asked permission to go to a cocktail party, "For just *one* martini, Mother!"

"My dear," replied her knowledgeable and experienced maternal parent, "There is no such thing as *one* martini."

The other two cocktail favorites are the *Manhattan,* and the *Old Fashioned.* Approximately the same arithmetic applies to their alcoholic content. They look different, though; and they taste different. Their effect is comparable to the martini.

You now have a sound working knowledge of what most people who drink at all in America today do drink, and what these drinks consist of. Most important, you know *how strong* these drinks are, in terms of alcohol content. You know from Chapter One that there are certain times and conditions when it is inadvisable to drink at all (on an empty stomach, for example; or too early in the day).

But there is still much to learn. In our next two chapters let us listen with open minds to what both sides of the drinking controversy have to say.

And it's not an "either/or" proposition. You don't have to base your decision about drinking upon either one or the other arguments that I'm about to present to you. In fact, I'd rather you didn't swallow either argument whole. But think about the facts and opinions as they are presented—then make up your mind.

If after reading the next two chapters and digesting them in your own way you still feel uneasy I'd suggest that you inspect one or two of the books on the subject listed in our *Suggested Readings* section beginning on page 93.

In the final analysis, then, the big question, *To drink or not to drink* will be answered by You—after a sensible consideration of the best evidence available. You'll be more confident either way, no matter what you decide. It will be your decision . . . and your responsibility.

CHAPTER *3*

"All Those in Favor"

The flowing bowl—whom has it not made eloquent? Whom has it not made free, even amid pinching poverty?

—HORACE

As we have seen, the use of alcohol beverages is an extremely old custom and, in some cultures, an honorable custom. The Old Testament attitude toward the use of alcohol was a tolerant one. Excessive drinking and drunkenness itself was condemned as it has been everywhere and at all times, but the use of wine—general in Biblical times—was considered acceptable. Moderation in this as well as in other kinds of social and individual behavior served as the standard in those days.

We recall the advice given to Lemuel, King of Massa, to whom it was said, ". . . . Give strong drink unto him that is ready to perish and wine unto those that be of heavy hearts. Let him drink, and forget his poverty, and remember his misery no more" (Prov. 31:6,7).

We also recall that the Psalmist praises the Lord for "He causeth the grass to grow for the cattle, and herbs for the service of man; that he may bring forth food out of the earth; and wine that maketh glad the heart of man . . . ."

Therefore we see that wine was regarded as one of God's gifts, to be used wisely with that same degree of acceptance expressed in the Proverb, "The earth is the Lord's and the fullness thereof."

We know that social and festive drinking has been approved by societies all over the world throughout the ages.

The wassail bowl of Merrie Olde England was a fixture in Shakespearean days, and we see many old prints and pictures of Elizabethan banquet tables showing the "cup lifted on high" and everyone apparently having a wonderful time.

There seems to be no doubt that the moderate use of alcoholic beverages has always been a great "socializer"; that is, a glass of wine or beer or mixed drink has been used from time immemorial to reduce social tensions and promote easier relationships between people. Sometimes "good fellowship" almost seems to depend upon the mutual, moderate use of alcohol.

But even aside from social "occasions"—gatherings at which people meet for the first time, celebrations, even religious rituals —certain kinds of beverage alcohol have for many centuries been integral parts of a culture's daily life. In many European countries practically no meal is served, even breakfast, without a glass of wine.

There are still areas in Europe where the drinking water and milk are unreliable, and the people depend upon wine for their daily beverage. It supplies the daily intake of sheer liquid necessary to maintain human health. Their digestions are almost as dependent upon the use of wine as a beverage as they are upon solid food for bodily nourishment.

Incidentally, alcoholism, or the *abnormal* use of beverage alcohol, is much more rare in these countries than it is in countries which do not traditionally rely upon these drinks at mealtime.

These are, mainly, the Latin countries—Italy, Spain and Portugal—and some of the smaller countries in Western Europe.

The Germanic countries—Germany, Austria, and the Middle European countries behind the Iron Curtain—are almost as dependent upon their brewed beverages, beers and ales, as are the wine-drinking countries on their sherries and ports. The conventional old German burgomeister wouldn't dream of sitting down to a meal without his foaming stein of beer, and his neighbors throughout the Scandinavian countries—Denmark, Norway and Sweden—agree with him most heartily.

Other countries are just as insistent that their meal simply wouldn't be complete without some form of distilled spirit. Some Middle-Eastern people, notably the Lebanese (about half of whom are Christian rather than Moslem), regard their native *arrack* as being quite indispensable before dinner; the Greeks drink *ouzo* before their evening meal. And in addition to their liking for beer and wine, some of the previously mentioned peoples like spirituous liquors before, during, or after their evening repasts: the Germans are fond of their *schnapps;* Scandinavians drink *aquavit;* and the Latins and the French vary their diets with *pernod, grappa* and other potions much stronger than their regular staples of wine and beer.

The British, including the English, Scots, Welsh, Irish and British subjects throughout the world (Australians, New Zealanders, Canadians), drink a great deal of both beer and whisky. The after-work, or bedtime, glass of beer, ale, porter, stout, or " 'arf-an'-'arf" in the neighborhood "pub" is as much an English tradition as is the famous "roast beef of England." In all parts of the Commonwealth, and especially in the United Kingdom, a "peg"—British slang for a short drink of neat whisky—is considered to be a *must* on almost any occasion; and we are reminded of Henry Aldrich's famous poem, "Five Reasons of Drinking":

> If all be true that I do think
> There are five reasons we should drink:

> Good wine—a friend—or being dry—
> Or lest we should be by and by—
> Or any other reason why.

In our own country, the traditions of drinking are by no means so clear-cut.

In the first place, we are a nation of many nationalities. These nationalities, the backbone of our nation and living proof that we are truly still the "Land of the Free," have brought along their own traditions of drinking, and in many instances, kept them intact in spite of outside influences such as Prohibition, economic depressions, and cultural and religious taboos militating for and against nationalistic customs.

In Yorkville, New York City's largely German section, the most popular drink is still beer. In "Little Italy," as we might suspect, wine is still the favorite beverage. Along Third Avenue, where bars are more apt to be named The Shamrock, The Dublin, or Finnegan's Grill, there are many calls for Irish whisky, of course.

This distribution of drinking customs is a nationwide phenomenon. In the Midwest, where there are many Americans of Scandinavian and Teutonic origin and descent, beer is by far the biggest-selling alcohol beverage. In the wine country of California, where it is no accident that a large Italian population has concentrated, people drink a great deal of wine. In the East, where populations are more mixed, sectional drinking habits are not so clearly indicated.

Only in the South does drinking custom seem to be indigenous. Certain habits observed below the Mason-Dixon Line seem to have originated there and to remain uniquely Southern.

The mint julep of Kentucky, for instance, is a tradition and even a symbol of the Old South's gracious way of life and its famous Southern hospitality. The julep, a tall cold mixed drink, is made of bourbon, mint, sugar and water—with the accent on the bourbon.

We have already spoken of the South's corn whiskey; today straight bourbon and bourbon and gingerale or bourbon and Coca-Cola (which originated in Atlanta, Georgia) remain favorite drinks. Still other drinks which are popular in other warm climates are popular in our own Southern states too: Tom Collinses, Rum Colas, Cuba Libres, Gin and Seven Up, and others too numerous to mention.

The foregoing provides us with a general idea of what Americans drink today. But what we want to consider at this point of our education on alcohol is: *Why do some people think drinking is a good idea?*

We have intimated that past generations as well as many representatives of the present one consider alcohol beverages to be conducive to good fellowship—a "tension reducer" in social gatherings, especially when strangers meet for the first time. There is nothing better, these people say, than a warming highball or glass of wine or beer to make people "loosen up," become more friendly and spontaneous, and in short to make a party a *party*—not just a gathering of self-conscious people.

As we have already seen, one of the main functions of alcohol is to "release the brakes" on the individual's personality (and, therefore, put him more at ease), so we can readily understand why these proponents of social drinking have a point in their favor.

Other advocates of normal, moderate drinking have stated their belief that social drinking is actually an outward sign of trust in one's fellowman; an expression of good faith and friendship. With real friends, they feel, one can afford to release the brakes a bit and be one's self a little more naturally and trustingly.

(Some ardent advocates of drinking even go as far as to say they don't trust people who don't drink: they think that nondrinkers can't or won't *trust themselves* when even slightly under the influence of alcohol.)

Possibly the most prevalent reason given in favor of drinking in the United States today is that it is a relatively harmless way of relaxing in a world of fears and tensions. We see businessmen in railroad cars going from their offices to their homes relaxing— "unwinding" is the current phrase—with a tall drink and a little convivial conversation with their fellow commuters. Others prefer to stretch out in a favorite easy chair with a pre-dinner cocktail and a chat with wife and children. This custom, they maintain, makes life in general much easier and much more pleasant. And what's the harm in it?

Still others wait until the weekend to do their drinking. When the Joneses drop over from next door to go bowling or for a game of cards, the bottles or cans of beer are opened almost automatically and everyone seems to enjoy himself all the more.

In some segments of our society, drinking has amounted to a statement of maturity, a "sign of manhood."

"A gentleman," we are told, "holds his liquor like a man."

It follows that failure to do this is a sign, somehow, of immaturity and unmanliness. Thus drinking becomes, in some people's eyes, a good test of character and behavior. This has been true over the ages, in many countries:

> Nor drunk is he who from the floor
> Can rise alone and still drink more . . .
>
> Nothing equals the joy of a drinker
> except the joy of the wine in being drunk.
>
> So I'm for drinking honestly, and dying
> in my boots.

The three quotations are from Thomas Love Peacock; from Maurice des Ombiaux, a French writer; and from John Masefield, England's Poet Laureate.

Shakespeare has said, "Drink down all unkindness"; Kipling extols "Somewheres east of Suez" (where a man can raise a

thirst); and Lord Byron becomes quite lyrical in praise of wine
when he writes:

> Fill the goblet again! For I never before
> Felt the glow which now gladdens my heart to
> Its core.
> Let us drink—who would not?
> Since through life's varied round
> In the goblet alone no deception is found.

The last line reminds us of what is likely the most famous of
all lines concerning alcohol drinks, the Latin maxim: *In vino est
veritas*—In wine there is truth. Whether or not this is true has
been argued back and forth for years.

These fragments of verse and quotations of famous men serve
to show us that drinking has been, and still is, regarded by many
wise and responsible people as a good and valuable practice—always with the addendum: in moderation. (It is next to impossible to find responsible advocates of drunkenness or excessive
use of these beverages.)

We can hardly deny that there is, under certain circumstances,
a certain hearty, robust attitude being expressed by these drinkers: the good fellowship, the carefree hoisting of a few tankards
of friendly ale, the trusting, almost brave gesture of quaffing
deeply of nature's wine and spirits—all this seems somehow to
be adventurous, manly and, perhaps, a part of growing up. We
could almost seem to measure a man's maturity as a "real" man
by the manner in which he has learned to "hold his liquor."

Many brave and honorable leaders of men through the ages
have been among "those in favor."

Oliver Cromwell drank both English ale and French wine;
and his great rival, Prince Rupert, liked the strong Hungarian
wines, especially Tokay. Frederick the Great preferred French
wines.

Two thousand years before Frederick, Alexander the Great

had his Cypriot wine shipped to him along his line of march from Macedonia to the Himalayas. Julius Caesar's favorite wine was Falernian, a red wine found close to Rome. He drank it mixed with water and cooled in snow.

Peter the Great of Russia drank brandy freely, and to decline to drink with him was tantamount to treachery.

Sir Francis Drake took Sack, a sherry-like brew from the Canary Islands, and Lord Nelson drank Marsala from Sicily. Napoleon was a regular consumer of Chambertin, a red burgundy.

Cortez, the conqueror of Mexico, favored a red wine made in Guadalcanal in La Mancha, Don Quixote's country, which gave the name to the now famous island in the Pacific.

It might even be argued that drinking could be used as a good test to determine one's "mental, emotional, and social adjustment," or general psychological health. If one can drink moderately and behave well after a few drinks he *might* be safe in concluding that he's pretty well in control of himself; he is "master of his fate and captain of his soul" as the saying goes. Well . . . maybe. We shall save this sort of discussion for later. However, it has been advanced as a possible reason for drinking, just as the opposite kind of behavior (*lack* of control when drinking) is an argument against it.

Then, too, some physicians and psychiatrists think that the moderate use of alcohol is psychologically useful as a kind of safety valve: they feel that this easy-to-obtain, relatively harmless "tranquillizer" tends to prevent tensions from building up to the point when they might injure the individual physically, mentally, or emotionally. They readily admit that in some Shangri-la where everyone is serene and happy such a tranquillizer would not be necessary or desirable, but since we unfortunately do not yet live in such a world, perhaps "a wee dram" now and then is indeed a blessing to those who need it, *if* they can hold their ration to the wee dram.

And now may be the best time to make clear what we mean by "normal" drinking or "moderate" drinking.

First, we must warn the reader once again that what is normal for one person may not be normal for another, hence the applicability of the old Latin saying: *Quod ali cibus est aliis fiat acre venenum.**

Also, what may have been moderate drinking for you on one occasion may be disastrous drinking on another.

However, there are certain reliable rules which you may follow, bearing in mind always that both the physiology and psychology of drinking are complicated affairs—simply because we humans are so complicated.

The National Safety Council Subcommittee on Intoxication has said, for instance, that a percentage of 0.05 (or below) of alcohol in the bloodstream is so slight as not to influence most persons one way or another as far as drinking is concerned.

Between 0.05 and 0.15 percent alcohol in the blood affects *all* individuals to some extent.

This amounts to from about one to three ounces of whiskey, two to six ounces of wine, or (approximately) one to three bottles of beer *per hour* taken after or during a meal.

Above this amount (0.15):

Everyone is definitely under the influence of alcohol

THEREFORE . . . if you take, roughly speaking, as much or more than three highballs or two cocktails, two goblets of wine, or three bottles of beer during any given hour, especially on an empty stomach, you are playing Russian Roulette with a revolver that has more than one deadly bullet in its cylinder. You can't even be sure (until, perhaps, it's too late) just what your percentage of safety is. You only know the cards are stacked against you.

Professional gamblers would tell you not to be a sucker.

As scientists, we can only say, Here are the mathematical

* "What is food to one may be fierce poison to others." Lucretius IV, 637.

probabilities for your information and guidance. Let your conscience (and your intelligence) be your guide.

Finally, we may cite the opinion of still another physician,
Dr. Kenneth Walker, who has written that "if he were a mil-
lionaire he would endow the United Nations with a sidewalk
café where the diplomats could sit, sip sherry, and make amica-
ble compromises instead of the usual strident speeches." *

Summarizing, we shall review the arguments in favor of drinking by enumerating them one by one:

1. The moderate use of wine was acceptable in Biblical days,
and it was regarded as a gift of God to be used wisely and well.

2. Drinking is an old social custom which has permitted people to relax together and become more friendly.

3. Alcohol beverages have been and still are widely used at
the table for the family's mealtime drink.

4. Wine has been and still is (in some countries) a substitute
for water and milk.

5. Moderate drinking is a relatively harmless way of relaxing
in a tense world.

6. Moderate, "civilized" drinking may be an index of mature
behavior and serve as a symbol of adulthood among many social
groups.

7. The *normal* use of alcohol may indicate a person's good
health and normalcy all around.

We know, of course, that some of these arguments might not
have much importance for the young person who is considering
the pros and cons of his own attitude toward drinking, although
many young people have already reached the point where the
tensions of the world have great direct impact upon them.

But—the young person considering drinking now will be the
world leader of tomorrow and what he decides now is of the ut-
most importance, to the nation and the world, and to the indi-

* From the article "Dear Son: If You Must Drink . . ." by Arthur Gordon
in the March, 1960, issue of *Better Homes & Gardens.*

vidual person himself. AND—what he decides NOW may very well be the deciding factor in his drinking pattern, his attitude toward drinking, and his feelings for the rest of his life toward those who drink. This is why we want to present the fairest and most complete picture possible of the whole subject. It is that important.

We know that some of our most revered leaders in all walks of life have been moderate users of alcohol. Others have been total abstainers. We want you to have all the facts now made available through modern science and education so that you can make the best possible decision for YOURSELF.

No one, we think, no group, could ask for anything more.

So now we shall give the opposing group "equal time," as the political parties say about radio and television debates.

With all of the preceding things so *good* about drinking, what's so bad about it?

Remember now, the idea is that you're going to make your decision concerning drinking on the basis of a logical, scientific inquiry into the proposition.

It wouldn't be cricket to drop this book and dash out to your nearest tavern keeper with the demand that he "fill the goblet again!"

He'll wait. The little brown jug will keep.

If your mind is already made up that you're going to start drinking (or to continue drinking, as the case may be) neither the arguments to follow nor anything else is going to stop you, you know that.

But if you read on and decide honestly that you can't accept the "All Opposed" point of view you'll enjoy your drinking lots more.

On the other hand, you might spare yourself a few quite unnecessary guilt feelings, not to mention a horrendous hangover.

We'll see.

CHAPTER 4

"All Opposed"

In vain I trusted that the flowing bowl
Would banish sorrow, and enlarge the soul.

—MATTHEW PRIOR

One of the first arguments the young person hears against the use of alcoholic beverages, even in moderation, is that it is detrimental to the performance of athletics. No baseball, football, basketball or track coach will approve of his team touching alcohol in any form, even a glass of beer with meals.

Even adult professional athletes must go in training for their events, whether they be Olympic Games, professional prizefights, or a pro football season. And training inevitably means . . . no drinking.

Why is this, in view of the fact that we've already decided that moderate drinking is, by and large, not harmful to the human body?

Here's why. The idea of alcohol or anything else being "not harmful" does not mean that maximum efficiency of performance would not be, temporarily at least, impaired by its use—no matter how moderately used.

To use an oversimplified example for the purpose of illustration, everyone would agree that, under ordinary circumstances, a glass of wine or beer or a mild highball before dinner would be classified as moderate drinking. But—that same drink, taken before the Big Game would be another story altogether. To say the least, an attack of indigestion might ensue. More likely, the athlete's finely developed coordination would be below its peak efficiency. The performer wants to be alert, not too relaxed; competitive, not sociable—for the duration of the game at any rate.

Also, famous coaches and trainers tell us that even the mildest form of drinking is bad for stamina; for our senses of distance and timing; and for our general overall physical and mental "tone."

They know that when they get a man, or a team, "up" for an event, the relaxing effect of alcohol will in most cases get him right back "down" again. There have been many tragic cases in the history of athletics where temporarily broken training has resulted in a permanently broken athlete. Big games have been lost, big individual competitions "blown," because of a few ill-advised, "harmless" drinks during the training period before the opening whistle blew.

Athletics by no means provide the only situations when human performance must be at peak level or else the performer sustains disastrous results. The musician, the debater, the actor—any practitioner of the performing arts, in fact—must make sure that his physical condition, mental alertness, aesthetic sensitivity, the coordination of his *total being*, are unhampered by the anesthetic effects of ethyl alcohol.

Even so routine (but oh so important, sometimes!) a matter as a classroom examination usually requires that we be "all there" —and not trying to cope with the additional handicap of fighting the sedative effect of last night's alcohol.

DRINKING AND DRIVING

This is such an important "performing art" that it deserves a section all to itself.

Drinking and driving is, at all times, literally a matter of life and death. And if you don't learn and REMEMBER anything else in this book except the following facts and figures, we urge you to learn and remember *them*.

You've all heard the familiar slogan of the National Safety Council: *The Life You Save May Be Your Own!* Well, the lines you are about to read may someday turn out to be the lines that saved that life—whether the life be yours or someone else's.

According to Ken Purdy, dean of American automotive writers and author of *Young People and Driving* (John Day, 1967), "Very few people under 25 years of age, and one might better say, under 30 years of age, *know* to the necessary half-ounce their capacity for alcohol. This is an area in which misjudgment can be literally fatal."

Everyone knows that "Alcohol and Gasoline Do Not Mix." We know all about "If You Drive Don't Drink. If You Drink, Don't Drive." And although we have placed our whole section on Drinking and Driving in our chapter entitled "All Opposed," we may be sure that here is one proposition on which all sides agree. Even the most devoted advocate of normal drinking is opposed to drinking of any sort while driving an automobile or any other vehicle.

The National Safety Council Subcommittee on Intoxication has recommended, and many states agree, that even a very small amount of alcohol in the bloodstream is enough to classify the drinking driver as being "under the influence" of alcohol. For instance, *any* person under *any* circumstances who has 0.15 percent alcohol in his blood is definitely under the influence. Many states employ scientific devices, known variously as the Drunkometer, Intoximeter, or Alcometer, to test the percentages of alcohol in the systems of arrested drivers. These machines cannot be fooled, and evidence obtained by their use are accepted in most courts of law.

As Raymond G. McCarthy, Director of the Division on Alcoholism, New York State Department of Mental Hygiene, points out in a leaflet entitled "Alcohol and Highway Safety":

> Highway traffic today presents a situation of intense competition, yet anyone above a certain age can get a driver's license. Licensing tests measure only the most elementary skills. They do not indicate the ability of the driver to handle a car under difficult conditions, for example, in heavy traffic. A driver's license is not evidence that the operator will be able to respond skillfully in an emergency. Many poor drivers never have an accident because they are never caught in a real emergency situation.
>
> There is evidence that even a very small amount of alcohol in the blood will lower the skill of a good driver. It can seriously disorganize the efficiency of an average or poor operator.
>
> Drinking and driving involves chance. Driving efficiency is lowered, depending upon the basic skills of the operator and the amount of alcohol in the blood. Chance determines whether an emergency will arise which the operator might be able to handle without alcohol but which leads to a serious accident if he has been drinking.

Are you willing to take this chance?

If you are, the smartest students of "chance" today—professional mathematicians and professional gamblers—would say one thing about you: *Stupid.*

Now it might be argued by a few hasty, illogical young people that they have a "right" to take that chance with their lives if they want to.

The answer to that is that no one has a right to endanger *other people's lives,* no matter *what* the argument might be on the "rights" of committing suicide. This—the whole business of knowingly taking a drink and proceeding to operate a vehicle in public—is not merely stupidity, *it is willingly taking a chance on committing murder.* Worst of all, it is an *unnecessary* chance. Sometimes in our mechanized society it does seem to be necessary to drive. It is hard to conceive of a situation in which it is necessary to drink.

The writer recalls a tragic incident in which he was an unwilling and shocked participant some years ago in the State of Georgia.

I had stopped at a roadhouse for dinner while driving from one city to another on a Saturday night.

At the roadhouse there were two parties of young people, enjoying themselves on their night off from studies. They were laughing, dancing occasionally to the music of a jukebox, and bursting into some pretty off-key harmonizing every now and then. They were having a wonderful time and I enjoyed watching them while I ate my dinner.

I noticed that one or two of the boys were drinking beer; the rest seemed happy enough with Cokes or coffee. No one was intoxicated by any stretch of the imagination.

One party broke up before I finished eating; the other shortly after.

I paid my bill and resumed my journey.

I had driven just a few miles when I came upon both cars. A pale and frightened young man was waving me to stop. One car was on its top; the other on one side. I sent the young man down the road to summon help, and began the sickening task of pulling young bodies out of the wreckage.

The passing years have mercifully obliterated my memory of most of what transpired during the next hour, but one thing happened that I shall never forget.

One of my headlights was shining on an object resting near one of the cars and I saw that it was a girl's shoe. I picked it up, thinking it might be useful for identification purposes later on. It was too heavy though for a girl's shoe, and I looked again.

Her severed foot was still in it. . . .

And the boy crumpled over the steering wheel of one of the cars was one of the boys who had been drinking beer. I recognized him at once by his sweater. He had spilled some of his beer on it during one of the songfests and had been most upset. . . .

The morning papers said that two passengers had been killed and four others injured in the accident. I remember that both of the dead had been boys. I've often wondered about the girl whose shoe I picked up.

Now I know it's possible that the tragedy might have occurred anyhow, beer or no beer. But when years later I read about the percentage of chance involved with drinking and driving that I've just shown you, I couldn't help but remember that ghastly night on a lonely Georgia highway.

And, of course, driving is not the only way in which we expose ourselves to danger almost every day of the week. Many of us, especially boys and men, operate machinery—in school shops, on the job, in the basement do-it-yourself shop—which can chop off a few fingers or mangle an arm with no warning at all. And there's nothing like a few drinks to increase our chances of just this happening.

This is not to mention the careless use of electricity—which all of us handle every day of our lives.

It goes without saying that even the best of us would be the least bit more careless with electricity *after* a glass of beer or wine or a highball than we would be *before* taking it. Unlike a hangover—during which we may learn a lesson and swear off forever (at least until the next time!)—a few hundred volts of grounded electricity doesn't give us this second chance. It can be rather like offering to give the pilot his money back if his parachute doesn't open.

All of these facts and figures have been impressed upon people both young and old for many years. Horrible illustrations have been given time and again; and sooner or later we have the unforgettable experience ourselves that teaches us our lesson about alcohol and safety. But let us try to make sure that we don't learn it too late. Hospitals, wheelchairs, and morgues are full of people who said: *But things like this never happen to ME!*

Finally, a word of understanding from a driver who happens also to be a psychologist.

I know that it's a great temptation to prove things for ourselves sometimes. In the laboratory and classroom, and in life itself, this can be a good and necessary thing if we are to learn about ourselves and the universe around us.

Furthermore, there comes a time when many of us—in spite of common sense and all the statistics in the world—find ourselves literally in the driver's seat, after we've had a drink or two.

This can be the most deceptive—and most dangerous—moment of our lives. Because it nearly always *seems* that we are driving better than we ever did! Our minds seem crystal clear, we are supremely confident, our timing and coordination are perfect. The whole business of "Drinking and Driving not Mixing" seems rather foolish.

But in the huge majority of cases we have to point out that the real keyword of the foregoing paragraph is "seems."

You *seem* to be driving better. You *think* your timing and coordination and judgments of distance are sharp and clear. You *feel* that you've got everything under control.

Well, science says that it just isn't so. No matter what we *seem* to be doing, or *think* is happening, or *feel* is the case, our old friend ethyl alcohol, C_2H_5OH, is still a depressant, still an anesthetic, still a narcotic, and its presence in our bloodstream is *depressing* us, *not* making us more alert. This can be, and has been, proved many times in scientific laboratories.

SOCIAL AND PSYCHOLOGICAL HAZARDS

In answer to the claims of "Those in Favor" that alcohol beverages may serve a useful function as a relaxing agent in social situations, "Those Opposed" point out that it can work both ways. What could be more embarrassing, for instance, than to "get a little too much" at a party and become disgustingly and conspicuously ill! Or even worse, "pass out" and have to be taken home! And it can happen to the best of us, say the anti-drinkers; without notice or fair warning. One Saturday night we may have three glasses of the "spiked" punch and feel fine. The next, we're hanging our heads in shame and feeling like Irvin S. Cobb's "wrath to come"—and on exactly the same amount of the same kind of punch taken at the same time of evening.

(We know enough about the physiology and psychology of alcohol now to realize that the complexity of the human consumption of such beverages renders it next to impossible to predict with any certainty just how we're going to react to alcohol at any given time. Remember how much depends upon the condition of the stomach, our emotional state, and so on.)

Others would insist that people, especially young people, shouldn't need an artificial "relaxer" for social situations: it would be far better, they say, to go to dancing school, or take a course in "How to Behave at a Party," or learn how to overcome that shyness and awkwardness in the school of experience sometimes referred to as the School of Hard Knocks. Besides, they contend, the use of such an artificial courage-bolsterer makes one dependent upon it, and the shy, awkward person never does learn poise and confidence in a social group. He relies on "bottle courage," and never develops any courage of his own.

This much should certainly be noted: it is no longer necessary to drink in order to be considered a good sport. It used to be true, most regrettably, that any person at a party or informal get-together, whether young or old, ran the risk of being called a "prude" or "scary-cat" or other equivalents of today's "square" or "chicken" if he or she declined to drink. This was one of the many unhealthy results of Prohibition: it became almost obligatory upon otherwise sensible, intelligent people to assert their "manhood and independence" by flaunting the law and drinking alcohol forbidden by the 18th Amendment.

Those days, thankfully, are in the past, except for certain dated movies we may see on television.

Nowadays there are numerous good excuses for not drinking, even at cocktail parties. Most people accept these reasons without question or embarrassment to the nondrinker. It is now quite simple and easy to say, "Sorry, but my doctor has advised me not to. You go right aread." Or, "My church is opposed to *my* drinking, so please excuse me, won't you? May I have a rum-and-coke *without the rum* instead, please?" Or, "Sorry, some other time. I'm in training for football, you know." Or, "Who needs alcohol in company like yours!" (For those who know, as we do, that alcohol is a depressant, this gambit is not recommended.)

You get the idea. Use your own reasons, they'll sound more spontaneous. But the idea is, it's perfectly all right not to drink if you don't want to drink. As a matter of fact, the writer recently heard one young girl, a high school senior, remark, "It's more distinctive *not* to drink these days!"

One vigorous DON'T:

Don't be "self-righteous" about your abstention from alcohol. Live and let live. Maybe your friends' doctors and ministers have told them that it's all right for them to drink; maybe they're *not* in training for football or for anything else. In any case, it would be deplorable manners to act superior about your tee-totalism and a surefire bet to lose friends and alienate people.

End of sermon on etiquette for today.

Now we can sum up these reasons against the use of alcohol beverages. There are many more, of course; but perhaps there were more good reasons *for* drinking, too. We've listed the main ones from each side of the drinking fence.

1. The drinking of alcohol is regarded as sinful by some churches. Their reasons must be given serious consideration. One's minister should be consulted in every case, and his counsel heeded.

2. Many physical-training authorities and athletic coaches believe that the use of alcohol, even as a mealtime beverage, is detrimental to human performance. Some music and art teachers concur in this opinion.

✱ 3. Alcohol can be a hazard to social success as well as an asset.

✱ 4. The use of alcohol to relieve social awkwardness tends to make the user dependent upon alcohol, rather than allowing him to learn the social graces naturally.

5. There is no real reason, no social need, for drinking at all. It is better to prove one's manhood and courage in other ways.

6. There are opinions and statistics which relate drinking to juvenile delinquency and crime.

7. There seems to be a relationship between some kinds of drinking and certain neuroses, or behavior disorders.

Undoubtedly the most serious arguments propounded against drinking are, however, these two:

1) The *incidence of crime and delinquency*—whether spontaneous, impulsive "crimes of passion" (such as injuring or even killing a person in a fit of uncontrollable anger); or premeditated, chronic crimes such as stealing—is much higher among young people who drink than among those who do not.

2) The *incidence of neurosis* (which we might classify as a "crime" against one's self) among those young people who drink to make their social and/or emotional problems seem more bearable rather than solving the problems themselves is much higher than among those who do not drink at all.

In the first instance it is easy to see how our explanation of "releasing the brakes on our behavior controls" would apply, as well as the business of "bottle courage" for those who do not avail themselves of other resources. It is much easier to fly off the handle after a few drinks; it is also easier to get up the courage (and dull the conscience as well) to participate in criminal action if one is already familiar with the use of alcohol than if one is a teetotaler.

In the second case, it should be obvious to all readers that the person who reaches for the glass of wine, beer, or liquor whenever something goes wrong is conditioning himself to depend upon alcohol, rather than learning how to cope with life normally and naturally. Yet, it seems to be an extremely easy thing to happen: a social humiliation; a failed exam; the anxiety preceding a public speech—one or two drinks and the world does seem better, and the drinker himself feels stronger and happier —temporarily. Tomorrow everything is the same; the real problem remains unsolved and must be faced after all. To put it still more succinctly:

There is no situation so bad that a few drinks won't make it . . . worse!

Or, the same fact of life summed up in different words:

Don't think things couldn't be worse. . . . Take a few drinks and they will be!

Finally, we must mention the question of sex and alcohol, and we're not sure whether to put this subject under the heading of Crime or Neurosis. It can lead to both if one is not careful.

Candy is dandy
But liquor is quicker!

This classic couplet is a flippant but all too true commentary on the relationship of beverage alcohol and sexual behavior.

As what we are concerned with here is education, not moralizing, we merely want to reiterate the scientific truth that one's behavior controls, one's *moral censors* so to speak, are "out on strike" after the minimum intake of alcohol we have already defined.

The point is, drinking in connection with sex-involved social situations may quite easily (and without fair warning) lead to sex behavior you wouldn't have wanted to happen if you hadn't been drinking. |

The problem of alcoholism is so important and so complicated that we must devote a separate chapter to it.

Alcoholism, however, is like Drinking and Driving—*both sides* are OPPOSED in no uncertain terms.

Nevertheless, fair play and scientific objectivity demand that we at least list these two aspects of drinking on the "Opposed" side of the ledger. It goes without saying that if there were *no* drinking, neither of the problems could exist.

Other problems might take their places, of course. Like smoking marijuana instead of drinking. Or using goofballs (barbiturates), or pep pills, or sniffing glue.

And these problems would be far more complicated, physically, mentally, emotionally and *legally* than drinking problems could possibly be.*

Let us stick to *solving* the use and abuse of beverage alcohol, then, and forget about dodging the issue by way of even more difficult "substitutions."

* See *Young People and Drugs,* by the present author. John Day, New York: 1969.

CHAPTER 5

"Lost Weekend"

Drunkenness is an immoderate affection and use of drink. That I call intoxication is besides or beyond that order of good things for which God hath given us the use of drink.

—JEREMY TAYLOR

"Alcoholism—Disease or Disgrace?" is the name of a booklet the present writer published a few years ago and it is still being used by alcoholism agencies as one of their information pieces. In it I pointed out that the American Medical Association recognizes alcoholism as an illness and that the alcoholic is a sick person. The National Council on Alcoholism proves these beliefs and the belief that the alcoholic can be helped and is worth helping. Our own federal government agency, the U. S. Department of Health, Education and Welfare, has stated that "alcoholism is a public health problem and is therefore a public responsibility."

Up until now we have been largely concerned with describing and defining the drinking of beverage alcohol, with only a suggestion here and there that the real issue may not be the use of alcohol, but its *abuse*.

Alcoholism is a dramatic example of *abuse*.

What is alcoholism? Who is the alcoholic?

Since we are still devoted to our ideal of scientific objectivity, let us start at the best beginning of any logical consideration of a difficult subject and *define our terms*: What does the word "alcoholism" mean?

There are several good definitions available to us. Here are four brief ones, representing several authoritative points of view, and more or less in agreement:

1. *Alcoholism is a disease which manifests itself chiefly by the uncontrollable drinking of the victim, who is known as an alcoholic.*—Mrs. Marty Mann, Founder and Executive Director of the National Council on Alcoholism.

2. *Alcoholism is a physical allergy coupled with a psychological compulsion.*—Unofficial definition of Alcoholics Anonymous.

3. *Alcoholism is progressive and is characterized by uncontrollable drinking.*—E. M. Jellinek, Sc.D., former Consultant on Alcoholism, World Health Organization.

4. *An alcoholic is anyone whose drinking interferes frequently or continuously with any of his important life adjustments and interpersonal relationships.*—Rev. Howard J. Clinebell, Jr., in *Understanding and Counseling the Alcoholic Through Religion and Psychology*.

The present writer would add that the word "control" is the key concept in either the description or definition of alcoholism. The alcoholic, at some point during his drinking experience, loses the ability to control the frequency and length of his drinking periods as well as the ability to control his actions when he is drinking.

Out of every fifteen or so persons who drink at all, one is going to become ill of the illness we call alcoholism.

There are about *five million* people in our country today who are in some stage of this illness, according to N.C.A.

Alcoholism ranks with heart disease, cancer, and mental illness as one of the nation's *four greatest public health problems,* according to the U. S. Public Health Service.

It has been estimated that alcoholism costs industry and taxpayers over a *billion dollars a year* in accidents, hospitalization, crime and many other by-products of the disease.

But before we go any further, let us examine the second part of our proposition: Alcoholism is an illness.

What do we mean by *illness* when we use it to describe alcoholism? It doesn't seem much like measles, or a virus, or heart disease. The alcoholic doesn't seem to "catch" alcoholism.

Yet if we look deeper we find that the trouble lies with our limited concept of the word "illness" rather than with the fact. We must think of illness in its broader, more meaningful interpretation if we are to understand the nature of alcoholism.

Here is the definition of illness given us by the American Medical Association:

> In general, any deviation from a state of health; an illness or sickness; more specifically, a definite, marked process having a characteristic train of symptoms. . . . Alcoholism does denote a condition in which there is a deviation from a state of health. Alcoholism can be classified into (1) primary alcoholism, which includes (a) those patients who from the very first drink of an alcohol beverage are unable to control their desire for it and (b) those who through use over a great many years have developed an inability to take a drink or leave it alone and have become like group (a); and (2) secondary alcoholism, which includes those who use alcohol for its sedative action as a means of escape from reality and, in particular, from their personal problems. . . . This secondary group comprises by far the majority of patients suffering

from alcoholism; however, most alcoholic patients prefer to be in the primary group.

The AMA definition, which is taken from *The Journal of the American Medical Association* (May 25, 1957), concludes by stating:

Regardless of which group an individual belongs to when under the influence of alcohol, he is ill.

Now the fact that the alcoholic is ill, is indeed the victim of a disease, means that he is not correctly looked upon as a person of poor character or of weak will.

The ex-president of the National Council on Alcoholism, Mr. R. Brinkley Smithers, has said: "Alcoholism is a *respectable* disease." By this he means that it is an illness which can strike any drinker, regardless of age, sex, social position, nationality, or religion. As a matter of illustration, there are clergymen from all faiths and denominations who have themselves become alcoholic in spite of being devout and dedicated ministers and priests of their churches.

Recent studies have shown that only 3 percent of America's alcoholics are Skid Row bums—97 percent of these unfortunate persons are intelligent, responsible, gainfully employed men and women.

So we now understand that we must not hold the alcoholic in contempt or as a subject for ridicule any more than we would make fun of a cripple or a person suffering from cancer.

The young person today, whether considering what to do personally about the question of drinking alcohol beverages or whether he has already made his decision, MUST, if he is to be properly informed about drinking in general, learn something about alcoholism. There are two major considerations:

1) What are the chances of *my* becoming an alcoholic if I drink? Can I detect any early symptoms which might indi-

cate that I'm a good bet for alcoholism? Would it be too late then to stop drinking and head off the illness?

2) What can I do to help those persons I know who have already become alcoholic?

Let us take them up one at a time.

First, we know already that if we drink, the chances are roughly one in fifteen that we shall have trouble with alcohol—perhaps become an alcoholic.

But this doesn't tell us much, does it? Is there some way, are there some clues which might give us a clearer picture of our chances?

Fortunately there are—if they are not taken too literally, and if we remember that they are just clues, not infallible predictions. Here are some of the things you should learn to recognize as danger signals.

1. Any feeling of dizziness, extreme feelings of elation, or unusual degrees of activity after a drink or two.

2. Feelings of depression or sadness; periods of silence, laziness, or extreme sleepiness after a drink or two or on the day after taking a few drinks.

3. Extreme shifts of emotion when drinking; for example, feeling unusually "down" one moment, and unusually "high" the next. Another example of this danger signal is the feeling of love and affection for a person, followed almost immediately by feelings of dislike and anger.

4. Feelings of carelessness: after a drink or two you "couldn't care less" about anything: you don't care whether "school keeps or not."

5. Ignoring or resenting the suggestion that you have had enough to drink, even if you know the advice is coming from a good friend who has your best interests at heart.

Generally speaking, the incipient alcoholic—the person who

seems to be in more danger of having serious trouble with alcohol if he drinks it at all—is the person to whom alcohol *seems to mean a great deal,* as opposed to the person who doesn't get very excited about drinking, one way or another; the person who can "take it or leave it alone."

As we have seen from the AMA's classification of alcoholics (page 71) some people find alcohol to be of great importance from the start, others develop this feeling over a period of years. For the young person just beginning to drink, the crucial lesson to be learned from these findings, made by doctors and other experts on drinking behavior over the years, is this:

An initial extreme liking for alcoholic beverages (or, more accurately, a liking for what the drinking of alcoholic beverages does for that person) is a DEFINITE DANGER SIGNAL.

If this danger signal happens to you the first time you have a drink or two (or at any time during your early drinking days) you should consult your physician or school psychologist at once before continuing to drink.

If reading our chapters on "Kinds of Drinks" and "All in Favor" made drinking seem extremely attractive to you—Beware! We have tried these chapters out on a number of people before going to press and found almost without exception that those whose "mouths were watering" after reading these passages were the very individuals who were heading for trouble with alcohol. Let these chapters and your reactions to them serve as guides to normal drinking OR as warning signals NOT to drink—as the case may be.

Dr. Ruth Fox, a psychiatrist and Medical Director of the National Council on Alcoholism, recently had these words of wisdom for the young person:

There is nothing necessarily destructive in their [young people's] observing that alcohol can relax certain tensions and improve a parent's mood. If, however, they get the impression that this is the *only* way to achieve gaiety or ease weariness and depression, they are absorbing some unfortunate ideas about both alcohol and the trials of grown-up life.*

One alcoholic of the writer's acquaintance recalls that his first reaction to beverage alcohol was something like this:

"When I took that first drink, and then two or three more and began to feel the least bit high, I thought to myself, *Boy!* Where has THIS been all my life? All of a sudden life seemed rosy, and I made up my mind never to be without a drink when I wanted one.

"Furthermore," he continued, "I felt great the next morning! Where was this terrible hangover I was supposed to have? Why had people been scaring me with this bogeyman all my life? I felt wonderful!"

This same man says that he has wished a thousand times that he had suffered the worst hangover in the world after that first experience with alcohol. He might have avoided years of misery, illness, jails and mental institutions. Thankfully, he is now a healthy and happy member of Alcoholics Anonymous, a fellowship we'll learn about shortly.

As to the question of whether it is possible to stop drinking early in the game after one has recognized his danger signals, it must be answered with a qualification: *Yes*, especially if the person involved seeks and obtains competent professional help (physician, psychiatrist, psychologist, pastoral counselor). The question of *why* the person cannot seem to drink normally should be answered, so that he can, through increased self-understanding, apply this knowledge to this and other areas of his life. Taken early enough, as with any other illness or potential illness, it is much easier to prevent than it is to cure later on.

And just as your doctor or psychologist or minister will admire and respect your courage and intelligence if you discuss the mat-

* In an interview with Dorothy Barclay, "Straight Thinking About Drinking," *The New York Times Magazine,* Dec. 17, 1961.

ter with him before you even start to drink, he will regard you even more highly if you have the good sense and honesty to bring him your problem before it's too late. Of course many of us are fortunate in having wise and well-informed parents and friends who can provide the help we need. But—parents and friends are human beings too, and we can't reasonably count on them to know everything. Alcoholism has become a subject for serious study and consideration only recently (as compared with other problems ranking with alcoholism in importance and danger to both the individual and the community in which he lives) and we cannot expect everyone to be an expert. In fact, a word of warning is very much in order at this point: Alcoholism, like human psychology in general, most unfortunately seems to encourage almost everyone to believe he is an expert, especially when he isn't.

If you don't believe this, just ask that barman at the corner bar and grill, any taxi driver, or, for that matter, almost any person you happen to be talking to—and chances are that he'll be able to tell you all about alcoholism, and with a great show of being absolutely right.

It has been said most truly that the only people who *don't* know all about alcoholism and alcoholics are the scientists who have studied them professionally for a number of years, and who have worked clinically with these sick people both in and out of hospitals.

The moral of this warning is clear:

When in doubt, ask a professional person. If he doesn't know the answer, he'll say so and either find out the answer for you or refer you to someone who does know.

The real experts are:

Medical doctors, psychiatrists (who are also M.D.'s), priests and ministers who have received special training in alcoholism, and certain kinds of psychologists (who usually have Ph.D. degrees)—counseling, consulting, clinical and school psychologists.

This brings us to the second part of what we should all know about alcoholism.

What can we do to help those persons of our acquaintance who seem to be alcoholic? And remember, alcoholism is a "respectable illness" that can happen in the best of families—including yours. Also, when we say *help* we mean *help*—not harassment or righteous indignation.

First of all, we must make sure that he or she *is* an alcoholic, or is apparently heading in that direction.

Just as we gave you a few danger signals for the person just beginning to drink, we are now able to provide some clues which may reveal the true illness of the alcoholic or potential alcoholic. They are, naturally, much more clear-cut than our previous "symptoms," since they are more fully developed and have been studied at greater length by specialists in the field of alcoholism.

The following questions are based upon a questionnaire used by Johns Hopkins University Hospital to help persons learn for themselves whether they are alcoholic or not. You may use them as a rough checklist to determine whether or not a member of your family or a friend is or may be becoming a victim of this disease.

YES	NO	
——	——	Does this person drink before breakfast, especially on the morning after?
——	——	Does he (or she) seem to prefer drinking alone?
——	——	Does he lose time from work due to drinking?
——	——	Is his drinking harming his family in any way?
——	——	Does he seem to need a drink at definite times every day?
——	——	Do his hands tremble if he does *not* have a drink?
——	——	Does drinking make him irritable?

—— —— Does drinking make him careless of his family's welfare?

—— —— Does drinking noticeably change his personality? (Does he seem like a different person since he has been drinking? Is he a "completely different person" when he has "had a few"?)

—— —— Has his drinking caused him, to your knowledge, to complain of bodily ailments?

—— —— Does he complain that he doesn't sleep well when he has been drinking?

—— —— Does he seem more impulsive since he has been drinking: i.e., does he do things on the spur of the moment, whereas before he was deliberate and controlled?

—— —— Does he seem to have less self-control since drinking: outbursts of temper, etc.?

—— —— Does he seem less ambitious since drinking?

—— —— Does he *require* a drink to be able to enjoy social functions?

—— —— Is he more definite in his likes and dislikes (especially of other people) since drinking?

—— —— Does he seem "moody" as a result of drinking?

—— —— Is he harder to get along with than before drinking?

—— —— Does he seem less efficient in general since he began drinking?

—— —— Does he seem to prefer "lower environments" since drinking? (Does he frequent disreputable bars, and associate with people whom he would previously have considered to be his inferiors?)

—— —— Is his drinking hurting his reputation?

—— —— Has he ever seemed to suffer complete loss of memory during or after drinking?

If you have confidently answered YES to any of the questions there is a definite chance that the person you are concerned about *may* be an alcoholic, or at least may be in for trouble with his or her drinking.

If you answered YES to *two* of the questions, the chances are that he is an alcoholic.

If you answered YES to *three or more* questions, you can be pretty sure that you've got an alcoholic on your hands—remembering at once that he is a sick person, that he needs help, that he can be helped, and above all, that he is worth helping.

As one last indication of alcoholism we should like to add another frequent symptom of the illness.

The alcoholic is most apt to refuse to admit, even to himself, that he is one of the small percentage of the adult population who cannot, through no fault of his own, drink normally, even though he may have seemed to do so in the past.

Now, there are three major ways in which the sick alcoholic can be helped back to normal health and happiness. Here they are:

1. *Alcoholics Anonymous.* This fellowship, devoted entirely to helping those alcoholics who want to be helped, has been more successful than all other forces in aiding alcoholics to get sober and stay sober. A loosely knit fellowship of many independent groups throughout the world, "AA" is based upon its famous "Twelve Steps"; and its program of mutual recognition, mutual understanding, and mutual help by fellow alcoholics. It is estimated that some 350,000 alcoholics in over eighty countries have found sobriety and peace of mind in AA.

2. *Medical and Psychological Treatment.* Leading physicians, psychiatrists and psychologists everywhere now recognize alcoholism as an illness. Reports of new, improved drugs appear regularly in the scientific journals and are being used successfully in the treatment of this illness. Individual psychotherapy, group

psychotherapy, certain kinds of psychoanalysis and other treatment techniques have shown promising results.

3. *Pastoral Counseling.* The clergy has been increasingly concerned about alcoholism as an illness and has taken realistic steps toward training selected ministers, priests and rabbis in psychological counseling as well as spiritual guidance. Your church, then, as well as your doctor, offers help to alcoholics.

Now let us be more specific. What is the *first* step to take in our effort to help the sick alcoholic? *Whom* do we see? What exactly do we do?

The best first step to take, whenever possible, is to make a personal visit to your local Alcoholism Information Center. This may be an affiliate of the National Council on Alcoholism. Many states have programs for helping alcoholics and those persons trying to help them; other communities may have their own local councils or committees. In any case, your local telephone directory will give you the address and the number to call for information or immediate help, or both. Simply look in the "A's" under *Alcohol* or *Alcoholism,* and you'll be able to pick out the most appropriate office to contact.

And don't be embarrassed about it. These people know exactly how you feel, and they are trained to help you and the sick person you're trying to help. They'll admire your good sense and up-to-date knowledge and understanding of the problem. Many of these persons have had firsthand experience with alcoholism, either personally or with some loved one or colleague.

These general information agencies are sometimes called *referral agencies* because their main function is to refer you efficiently to the best source of immediate help: specialized physician, psychiatrist, psychologist, nearest group of Alcoholics Anonymous, hospital or church. They will also furnish you with dependable literature on the subject to help you decide the best step to take.

In some communities there are, in addition to regular groups of Alcoholics Anonymous, groups known as "Al-Anon" and

"Alateen." Al-Anon groups are intended for husbands and wives of alcoholics; Alateen groups are for young people who have the problem of alcoholism in their families, usually a mother or father.

Like AA itself, Alateen began with one person, a high school boy in California whose father was an alcoholic. The following "preamble," (edited and slightly abridged by the writer), has been suggested by an Alateen group in New York City as a possible beginning for group meetings and will serve to illustrate what Alateen is all about:

> Alateen groups are made up of young people whose parents are drinkers. They find that meeting with other young persons in similar circumstances is helpful. We realize that even though an alcoholic parent may have joined Al-Anon, we can play an important part in re-uniting the family.
>
> We urge you to try our program. We, in Alateen, have learned to become individuals. We try to accept the fact that alcoholism is a disease. In studying the Twelve Steps of Alcoholics Anonymous we can accept the fact that our alcoholic parents are powerless over alcohol, and that we can develop the ability to detach ourselves emotionally from our parents' problems, yet retain our love for them.
>
> Our changed attitude might possibly inspire the alcoholic to seek help which may eventually lead him to AA, so there is no need for discouragement even though the alcoholic may still be drinking.
>
> We try at all times to reassure our parents that we do not discuss *them* at our meetings. Our sole topic is the solution of our own problems.

In smaller communities having no such agencies, there is almost always an AA group, and it will be listed in the phone book. Don't hesitate to call that number. While AA members are not usually trained professionals, they *are* highly experienced in all phases of alcoholism, and most of them recognize their own limitations as laymen. They know doctors and hospitals and how to contact them quickly and get immediate action.

There is hardly a community anywhere, no matter how small or how remotely located, where it is impossible to find help for the alcoholic. There is always your own doctor, your minister, and your teacher to fall back on, and if they can't help you they'll know who can.

If it is more appropriate for you to write for information and help, here are three addresses that will furnish you promptly with everything you need:

AA—Alcoholics Anonymous (for men and women who want to stop drinking):
P.O. Box 459
Grand Central Station
New York 17, N.Y.

Al-Anon (for the families of alcoholics) and *Alateen* for children of alcoholics):
P.O. Box 182
Madison Square Station
New York 10, N.Y.

NCA.—The National Council on Alcoholism,
2 East 103 Street
New York 29, N.Y.

The important thing is: *do something*—but do it carefully, and with competent help. For instance, you might be doing your alcoholic friend or relative a great disservice by blundering into a delicate situation like a bull in a china shop. We are reminded of the rueful description of the "professional do-gooder" made by a wise old doctor some years ago:

"Some of these do-gooders, although well-meaning, are determined to do you good even if it kills you!"

This is why we urge you to make sure of your problem, then take it discreetly to a qualified person for guidance.

Perhaps the best advice can be summed up in two words said by a great scientist to the writer many years ago and which have stood the test of time: *Hasten slowly.*

Study your problem (the potential patient); *survey the tools at your disposal* (Alcoholics Anonymous; your church; etc.); then, *hasten slowly* (do something—carefully and with competent help).

And try to be patient with your patient. He is in the grip of something beyond the control of his will power. If he tries at all, give him all the encouragement you can muster. If he fails, try to ignore it and try again when the time seems right.

Even if all of the suggestions made in this chapter fail, there are still other resources—kinds of "Alcoholic Courts of Last Appeal," so to speak—which have cured even the most chronic cases of habitual uncontrolled drinking, as the present writer prefers to define "alcoholism."

If you have conscientiously tried all of the groups and agencies recommended above and your loved one's drinking is still out of control, you can always write to me in care of the publisher of this book and I'll arrange for you to get the help you need.

CHAPTER 6

Youth Speaks Out

Certainly alcohol problems are no respecters of individuals, regardless of race, creed, or color. Honest education on the subject for young people is an important part of their growing up together.
—JACKIE ROBINSON

In this chapter we are going to tell you about one organization's efforts to bring more and better education on alcohol to the secondary schools of America. As part of its program it invited leading educators and experts on alcohol from all over the country to participate in a symposium, or conference, to discuss the best ways of bringing unbiased, factual information on the subject to the young people of the U.S.A.

Even before the symposium took place (it was held in New York City) the Christopher B. Smithers Foundation, a charitable foundation whose major interests are in the fields of cancer and alcoholism, found that everyone concerned agreed that such education was desirable, but there was not much agreement as to how it should be done. This became the task of the symposium: to explore possibilities and exchange ideas on how to initiate the job.

Originally, Mr. R. Brinkley Smithers, president of the Foundation, conceived of the plan as being directed specifically toward alcohol education in the private secondary schools, because many state educational systems had already installed such programs in the public schools. General interest became so great, however, that it was decided to encompass all secondary schools in the study.

There was, in fact, considerable public interest in the symposium; a highlight being a nationwide discussion of the subject on the Rt. Rev. James A. Pike's (Episcopal Bishop of California) Sunday morning television program.

Mr. Smithers served as chairman of the symposium, which was supervised by Mr. Charles P. Frasier, Educational Director of the Foundation. The writer had the honor of serving as the moderator or master of ceremonies of the conference.

Among the principal speakers at the gathering were the late Raymond G. McCarthy; Dr. Mitchell Gratwick, Headmaster of New York City's historic Horace Mann School; Professor Clifford R. Brownell, Chairman, Department of Health, Physical Education and Recreation, Teachers College, Columbia University; Mrs. Vashti I. Cain, Department of Education, State of Mississippi; Dr. W. K. Ferrier, Educational Director of the Oregon Alcohol Education Committee; Dr. Mildred H. Weiss, Director of Psychological Services, Cleveland Center on Alcoholism; and Rev. Yvelin Gardner, Deputy Executive Director, National Council on Alcoholism.

And of special interest to the reader—and the big hit of the two-day symposium—a student panel consisting of a private school senior, a young man; a public high school junior, a young lady; a male junior from a preparatory day school; and a senior at Barnard College who had graduated from a private school for girls.

First, we shall give you a few key remarks of the educators and experts, then the comments of our student panel.

. . . Historically, social attitudes toward drinking range from toleration of drinking (but with sanctions against drunkenness) . . . to condemnation of drinking as being inherently evil . . . to the concept of the use of alcohol as an escapable fact of society. The schools have a responsibility to interpret the society in which their students are to function and if the use of alcohol is an unresolved issue, we must explore constructive attitudes—with the transmittal of sounder attitudes to succeeding generations of young people.

—Professor McCarthy, "Alcohol Education and Social Responsibility: A Review of Education on Alcohol Studies."

. . . Our policy is to present the facts [on alcohol] and allow the individual student to choose the facts that he thinks are important to him. . . . Alcohol education in the school should be undertaken concurrently with learning the drinking habits of parents, their attitudes toward their own and their children's drinking; the relevance of religious background and customs; the actual drinking habits (if any) of the students themselves and their motivations for drinking; and the attitudes of their own group as well as those of other groups.

—Dr. Gratwick, "Some Pros and Cons of Alcohol Education from the Administrators' Point of View."

. . . Education about alcohol deserves a prominent place in the school curriculum . . . *Education* is viewed as a process for the development of proper attitudes, habits, knowledges, and skills that involve experiences of great value *now, and* to prepare youth for *later* happiness and success—"To live most and serve best." *Alcohol education* falls into the category of subject matter designed to make human beings better able to cope with problems associated with wholesome personal and family living and responsible citizenry.

—Professor Brownell, "Alcohol Education and Public Health."

. . . Most young people are eager to learn about all aspects of growing up. Their need to know about alcohol is a real one. Aspects of alcohol education that demand special consideration include the social, cultural, and religious conflicts which are involved.

—Mrs. Cain, "How Mississippi Introduced Alcohol Education into the Public Schools."

. . . Every effort is made by our consultants to stress the fact that students must make their own decisions about drinking. Their role and that of the teacher is to supply them with information and give them an opportunity for research and discussion. We emphasize to the teacher the importance of developing and maintaining an objective, unbiased attitude regarding the use of alcoholic beverages by the adult citizen.

—Dr. Ferrier, "How Oregon Introduced Alcohol Education into the Public Schools."

. . . We divide our program into five areas: (1) Drinking—a Well-Established Social Custom; (2) What Alcohol Is and Where It Comes From; (3) The Physiology of Alcohol; (4) The Psychology of Drinking (why people drink and the psychological effects of drinking and (5) Alcohol and Social Problems.

—Dr. Weiss, "Methods and Techniques of Alcohol Education."

. . . Young people, whether in our church schools or elsewhere, must be approached on the matter of alcohol education from the position of *their own* attitudes—not on the basis of adult wishes, attitudes, and ideas. A proclamation of the National Council of Churches, "The Churches and Alcohol," points out that the churches should share a pastoral concern for alcoholics and their families, and on those relatively rare occasions when drinking reaches the point of alcoholism all resources of churches and pastors should be joined to aid the victim who cannot deal with the problem without help. . . . This points out that alcohol, as one of God's creations, has a purpose which is good, although its excessive use cannot be condoned. It is only through the coordinated efforts of the church, home, school, and the community that effective measures against alcoholism can be taken.

—Reverend Gardner, "Alcohol Education and the Churches."

THE STUDENT SPEAKS
(Student Panel)

Joseph S., senior, New York City private school: ". . . I don't drink, although my family does—normally and socially. Regarding alcoholism and drunkenness— Most of my fellow students still consider it more or less something to laugh at. It may be a disease, but most of the fellows consider it to be mostly weak will."

Pamela C., junior, Long Island public high school: "We are tested on our ideas of alcohol and alcoholism. As we go along, we find many of our original ideas were wrong. I think that later on this new knowledge will be of help to us. We don't laugh at it the way Joe's friends do. We know that alcoholism is a disease—that putting a man in jail for it does not reach the cause or change his attitude. I have noticed a big change even in one of the boys in my class who is usually a scoffer at all the teachers and who drinks himself. He has listened, and we have talked about alcohol freely, and there is a big change noticeable in him." *(Applause)*

Robert M., junior, preparatory day school: "I think we would appreciate a program on alcohol where we could go into it more deeply than just the physiology of alcohol, so we could see the social problems too. I think a textbook should be used so that the teacher could refer to it. Giving us the facts would also tend to help students' emotional problems coming out of the home relating to alcohol."

Elizabeth T., senior, Barnard College: "We did not have instruction on alcohol at the school I attended. I think that students *do* have a problem on the subject of alcohol when they get to college. The program that Pamela described was excellent. I feel that the ages of sixteen or seventeen—just before a student leaves for college—are an effective age at which to wage a campaign of this sort."

⬚‎‏

(The Student Panel received an ovation when these young people concluded their contribution to the symposium, and it was agreed that it was one of the most stimulating and challenging parts of the two-day program.)

During the informal discussions which followed, two particularly interesting facts emerged:

1) Surveys have revealed that from *one-third to two-thirds* of all high school students today drink beverage alcohol at one time or another, usually fairly regularly. Taking the lower figure just to be on the conservative side, a Purdue University Opinion Panel which questioned 10,000 high school students also found that twice as many high school seniors as freshmen drink. And a Minnesota poll reflected the strong belief that more young people between sixteen and nineteen drink today than before World War II.

2) One alarming study showed that *two out of three alcoholics began drinking in high school.**

It was agreed that education on alcohol in the secondary schools was in fact a highly desirable ideal, and President Smithers concluded the symposium by promising the full support of the Christopher D. Smithers Foundation.

We hope that the present book is in accordance with the goals and ideals that were established and clarified in the symposium we have just described. We have tried to meet all of the suggestions made by both the specialists in alcohol education and the professional educators—teachers and school administrators alike.

But as Dr. Weiss pointed out: "The real effectiveness of the symposium should be assessed by what *happens* rather than what is *said*."

The same is true of the present book. We have pointed out the basic things a young person in the mid-twentieth century

* Both references are from "Alcohol and the Adolescent," by Jean Libman Block, *Parents' Magazine*, published by The Parents' Institute Inc., 52 Vanderbilt Ave., New York 17, N.Y.

should know about beverage alcohol. What you do about these things is up to you.

We are almost at the end of our basic education on drinking. It remains only for us to review what we have learned, and to provide references for those who may be interested in further study. We hope we have kept our promise to give you information, verifiable information—not pep talks or sermons. We hope, too, that you are now able to say, somewhat like the member of Alcoholics Anonymous,

✳ "I'm no reformed drunk . . . I'm an INformed drunk!"

What *he* meant was, of course, that he had learned that he could never again drink normally and accepted this fact; he was not just "on the wagon" as the saying goes about drinkers who "swear off" drinking for a certain period of time.

What we mean for you is that you can now decide for yourself just what you want to do about drinking and that your decision will be based on *in*formation—not empty resolutions grounded in superstition or upon well-meant but misinformed advice.

In summary, we may repeat that:

1. Educators and experts on alcohol studies throughout the nation agree that Education on Alcohol in the secondary schools is a highly desirable subject for students—as the custom of drinking is a well-established fact of our society today. Every young person must decide for himself whether he is going to drink or not.

2. Figures indicate that from one-third to two-thirds of high school students drink alcoholic beverages fairly regularly. One study showed that two out of three alcoholics began drinking at high school age. On the other hand, nationwide figures indicate that perhaps half of our present high school students will drink as adults and that at least 97 percent will remain normal drinkers.

3. *The individual young person should consult his or her physician and minister or priest before beginning to drink.* What might be a harmless, even beneficial practice for one person might be a disastrous practice for another.

4. Everyone, it goes without saying, is opposed to the illness called alcoholism.

5. Everyone is opposed to drinking while driving.

6. Some people argue that if there were no alcohol, these problems could not exist.

7. Other people argue that it's the *drinker,* not the *drink,* that matters. These people feel that the great majority of drinkers should not be forced to quit drinking because a few people can't handle drinking safely and sanely.

Perhaps there should be a middle path between these two extremes. There are colors besides black and white on the alcohol beverage spectrum. There are many gradations of blues and reds and yellows.

Granting readily that the religious bodies and certain individuals who oppose the consumption of beverage alcohol in any form at any time have an inalienable right to do so on *religious* grounds, it would seem that other individuals must make up their minds about drinking on physiological, psychological, and sociological grounds.

It is these people for whom the present book is intended.

For them, perhaps, the question is not a simple "To drink or not to drink," but rather . . . *when* to drink—moderately. There are undoubtedly times when none of us should drink at all: when our doctor or minister or psychologist advises us not to; when driving or operating dangerous machinery; when we fear that we might be becoming alcoholic.

As far as all other times are concerned—that question, students of alcohol, is now UP TO YOU.

The writer and all those who joined him, directly or indirectly, in presenting these facts about drinking to you herewith offer you our vote of confidence:

On the basis of fact . . . not fallacy

On the basis of science . . . not superstition

and on the basis of your own good sense and goodwill toward others . . .

We think you will make the right decision for yourself.

SUGGESTED READING

(FOR THE GENERAL READER)

1. *Alcohol Problems, A Report to the Nation by the Cooperative Commission on the Study of Alcoholism.* Prepared by Thomas F. A. Plaut. Oxford University Press: New York, 1967.
2. Cain, A., *The Cured Alcoholic.* The John Day Company: New York, 1964.
3. ———, *Paul King's Rebellion.* The John Day Company: New York, 1967.
4. Chappel, N., *et al., The Use of Alcohol Beverages Among High School Students.* The Mrs. John B. Sheppard Foundation: New York, 1953.
5. Chavetz, M., *Liquor: The Servant of Man.* Little, Brown and Company: Boston and Toronto, 1965.
6. McCarthy, R., *Teen-Agers and Alcohol.* Yale Center of Alcohol Studies: New Haven, 1956.
7. ——— & E. Douglass. *Alcohol and Social Responsibility.* Thomas Y. Crowell Co., 1949.

(FOR THE PROFESSIONAL)

1. Block, M., *Alcoholism, Its Facets and Phases.* The John Day Company: New York, 1965.
2. Clinebell, H., *Understanding and Counseling the Alcoholic.* Abington Press: Nashville, Tenn., 1956.
3. Jellinek, E., *The Disease Concept of Alcoholism.* Hillhouse Press: New Haven, 1960.

4. Leake, C., & M. Silverman, *Alcoholic Beverages in Clinical Medicine*. Yearbook Medical Publishers, Inc.: Chicago, 1966.
5. McCarthy, R., ed., *Alcohol Education for Classroom and Community*. McGraw-Hill Book Co.: New York, 1964.
6. Monroe, M., & J. Stewart, *Alcohol Education and the Layman*. Rutgers University: New Brunswick, N.J., 1960.

ACKNOWLEDGMENTS

The contributors to the field of alcohol studies are so diversified and so numerous that it will be impossible to give thanks to all those who have helped the author write this book. I cannot close, however, without expressing my gratitude and indebtedness to at least a few of the leaders in Education on Alcohol whose names have not appeared in the text of the book:

Donald Horton, Ph.D., upon whose definitive work, *The Functions of Alcohol in Primitive Societies: A Cross Cultural Study,* I have relied most heavily in my section on History of Alcohol Production and elsewhere in the book. I have used Professor Horton's fine work so often over the years I am now no longer quite certain whether I am guilty of plagiarizing him, or am quoting him with academic propriety. In either case, perhaps he will forgive me in the present instance—since it is "in a good cause."

Professor Selden D. Bacon, whose brilliant and fearless administration of the Yale (now Rutgers) Center of Alcohol Studies has kept alive the spirit of eclectic scientific research on the many aspects of alcohol and its concomitant problems and benefits.

Professor Mark Keller and Miss Vera Efron, Quarterly Journal of Studies on Alcohol, Rutgers University, without whose tireless efforts we workers in the field could not function at all.

Mr. Thomas J. Donovan, President, Licensed Beverage Industries, who made available to me the fine library, archives, and other resources of the industry, and whose staff kindly consented to check my manuscript for accuracy without once attempting to influence my writing. The United States Brewers Association, Inc., was also kind enough to check my manuscript for factual content.

Participants in the Smithers Foundation Symposium

(Chapter Five)

Dr. William G. Carr, Executive Secretary, National Education Association.

The Reverend Thomas Huntington Chapell, Headmaster, The Hotchkiss School.

Miss Barbara Colbron, Headmistress, The Spence School.

Mr. Paul F. Cruikshank, Headmaster, The Taft School.

Dr. Frank E. Gaebelein, Headmaster, The Stony Brook School.

The Reverend H. M. Irvin, Jr., Episcopal High School, Alexandria, Virginia.

Mrs. George J. Johnston, Principal, Dana Hall School.

Mr. Thomas J. Johnston, Master, The Lawrenceville School.

Mr. David B. Koth, The Pingry School.

Dr. Harry V. McNeill, Consultant in Clinical Psychology, U.S. Public Health Service, Department of Health, Education and Welfare.

Mrs. Charles R. Maxwell, Jr., Executive Secretary, Parents League of New York, Inc.

Mr. Robert J. O'Donnell, National Safety Council.

Miss Esther Osgood, Executive Secretary, Secondary Education Board.

Mr. Simon O'Shea, Licensed Beverage Industry.

Mr. Francis Parkman, Executive Secretary, National Council of Independent Schools.

Mrs. Joseph P. Purtell, President, Parents League of New York, Inc.

Mr. Everett B. Raines, Moses Brown School.

Mr. J. Folwell Scull, Jr., Headmaster, Polytechnic Preparatory Country Day School.

Mr. F. Allen Sherk, Headmaster, Hopkins Grammar School.

Mr. William G. Schute, Development Officer, The Choate School.

Mr. Albert Thorndike, Chairman, Science Department, Milton Academy.